Astrophysics
KNOWLEDGE
IN A
NUTSHELL

Astrophysics
KNOWLEDGE
IN A
NUTSHELL

Sten Odenwald

ARCTURUS

Other books by this author:

The 23rd Cycle: Learning to Live with a Stormy Star
Patterns in the Void: Why Nothing is Important
The Astronomy Café: 365 Questions and Answers from Ask the Astronomer
Back to the Astronomy Café
My Astronomical Life: A first-person journey
Cosmic History II: From the Ice Age to the End of Time
Cosmic History: From the Big Bang to the last Ice Age
Eternity: A User's Guide
Interstellar Travel: An Astronomer's Guide
Interplanetary Travel: An Astronomer's Guide
Solar Storms: 2000 years of Human Calamity!
Exploring Quantum Space
A Degree in a Book: Cosmology
Space Exploration: A History in 100 objects

ARCTURUS

This edition published in 2019 by Arcturus Publishing Limited
26/27 Bickels Yard, 151–153 Bermondsey Street,
London SE1 3HA

ISBN: 978-1-78950-220-6
AD006805UK

Printed in China

Contents

Introduction

The investigation of the contents of our universe from the edge of Earth's atmosphere to the distant stars and beyond has traditionally been called 'Astronomy', although prior to the 16th century the term astrology was more commonly applied to this subject. Humans have always gone beyond merely noting the locations of the stars and planets in the sky as they tried to explain what they were seeing – but this was usually in terms of the only explanatory framework they knew: mythology or religion.

The character of these explanatory approaches changed dramatically when Johannes Kepler found regularities in the motions of the planets and tried to account for them in terms of various geometric theories. His first two laws were published in 1609 including the first law of elliptical motion. Less than a century later, Sir Isaac Newton succeeded in interpreting the movements of the planets in terms of the action of the force of gravity. This was the first, and very successful, attempt to explain astronomical events and situations in a physics-based theory of how forces interact with matter. In so doing, he created a new sub-discipline in astronomy we now call astrophysics. The most important feature of this new 'astro-physics' was that it was capable of making detailed mathematical predictions of what an astronomer should expect to see if the underlying physical theory and explanation was applicable.

Astrophysics is a subject that develops explanations for astronomical processes and the origins of the major objects in the universe in terms of the actions of forces upon matter, taking full advantage of the detailed mathematics-based theories in physics to show how astronomical systems are formed and evolve through time.

This book will highlight some of the major themes in modern astrophysics. It is a story of not just how things appear in space but why they have taken on these appearances as systems of matter evolving through time.

PART I

The Astrophysicist's Toolbox

Chapter 1

Observing the Universe

Since the dawn of the printed word, astronomical instruments have dramatically changed in their accuracy, purpose and appearance. From the simple theodolites and cross-staffs used in the 16th century, to the powerful space telescopes of the 21st century, astronomers have used a variety of tools to help them discover what lies beyond the earth.

THE ELECTROMAGNETIC SPECTRUM

One of the most powerful tools for observing the universe is the electromagnetic (EM) spectrum. The electromagnetic spectrum is a collection of photons sorted according to their increasing wavelength, which can be emitted by objects according to a variety of physical processes. By studying this EM radiation you can diagnose the kinds of physical processes taking place. For example, if a source is a powerful emitter of X-rays, you can tell that it contains very hot gases (called plasma) above temperatures of 100,000 k. If the spectrum follows a curved shape called a 'black body' you can immediately use this fact to take the temperature of the source. If the shape of the spectrum increases sharply to longer wavelengths, this implies there are electrons within the source travelling at nearly the speed of light within strong magnetic fields. Also, if the light appears as discrete, individual lines of emission, you know that the source is a translucent cloud of gas with emission from individual populations of atoms such as calcium, iron, oxygen and so forth.

The types of telescopes used to gather this EM radiation depend on the wavelength of the photons. At optical wavelengths such as those for which our eyes are sensitive near 500 nanometres, simple lenses and mirrors suffice to focus and reflect the EM energy. At much longer wavelengths measured in millimetres and centimetres, you need the technology of radio receivers in which large metallic parabolic 'dishes' are used to focus the radio-wavelength energy.

In addition to detecting faint objects, increasing the aperture of a telescope also greatly improves the resolving 'power' of the system. The basic formula for telescopes is

$$\theta = 206265 \, \frac{\lambda}{D}$$

where λ is the wavelength of light in metres and D is the diameter of the mirror (lens) in metres. The human eye has an aperture of about 5 mm (⅙ in) when fully dark-adapted, so at 500 nm its resolution for $\lambda = 500 \times 10^{-9}$ meters and D=0.005 meters is 30 arcseconds. A 15 cm (6 in) mirror, which is popular for amateur astronomers, can resolve features that are 1 arcsecond in size such as lunar craters 2 km (1¼ miles) in diameter. However, the turbulence and stability of the atmosphere can limit astronomical 'seeing' to about 1 arcsecond, smearing out details under twinkling starlight. It wasn't until the 1990s when computer and servomotor speeds had greatly improved that this 'adaptive mirror' technique could be widely employed to eliminate atmospheric twinkling. This technique is so effective that modern ground-based telescopes routinely out-perform the space-based Hubble Space Telescope for certain types of observations.

TELESCOPES AS 'LIGHT BUCKETS'

For millennia, we have learned about the universe by using ordinary human eyesight provided by a 5 mm (⅙ in) lens and an organic photodetector called a retina. But by adding a larger lens or mirror an instrument can be created, which greatly increases the number of photons entering the human eye. The single most important purpose of these instruments, called telescopes, is to collect as many photons of light as possible from distant sources, which is a function often referred to as that of a 'light bucket'. This function is proportional to simply the area of the telescope's primary objective. Large telescope mirrors (and optical apertures generally) increase the amount of light collected from dim objects allowing them to be studied in detail. The aperture of the human eye is only about 5 mm ($\frac{1}{6}$ in), and allows us to see stars in the sky as faint as the sixth magnitude ($+6^m$). By increasing the area of the objective lens or mirror, the brightness limit increases by 5 magnitudes for every 100-fold increase in area. Within the neighbourhood of the sun, most stars are between magnitudes of $+6^m$ and $+15^m$, while the dimmest stars and galaxies in the visible universe are typically at magnitudes from $+20^m$ to $+30^m$. To study them we need the largest apertures we can build to gather their faint light, and this is why astronomers are relentlessly building larger telescopes.

Refracting telescopes use a large *objective lens* at one end of a cylindrical tube, and a set of smaller lenses at the other end of the cylinder called the eyepiece. The Galileo telescope of 1609 had a magnification of about 21× with an objective lens about 37 mm (1½ in) in diameter, while the largest refractor at the Yerkes Observatory built in 1895 has an objective lens 102 cm (40⅛ in) diameter. Refracting telescopes of any appreciable size are difficult to make because of the number of optical surfaces that need to be precisely polished to focus light. Also, they are supported around their circumference so the massive objective lens of the Yerkes Refractor, which weighs 250 kg (55 lb), sags at its centre, causing optical changes as the telescope is moved. This limitation is the major reason that the construction of large refractors was abandoned in the 20th century.

Reflecting telescopes use a large mirror, or collection of mirror segments, to reflect light to a focus where an eyepiece can be inserted to magnify the image. Since only the front surface of the primary mirror has the required parabolic curve with a reflective surface, the entire rear side of the mirror can be used to support the weight of the mirror without compromising the optics. Isaac Newton's first reflector in 1668 had a metallic primary mirror, an aperture of 15 cm (6 in) and a magnification of 40x.

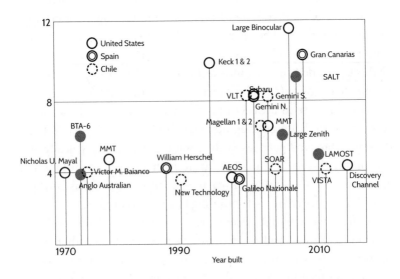

The evolution of telescope size showing the equivalent diameter of the primary mirror in metres (vertical axis).

The low cost and exceptional light-gathering ability of reflecting telescopes quickly made them the most desired optical instruments for astronomical research. Initially the primary mirrors were a single piece of glass weighing several thousand kilograms, but a new 'segmented-mirror' approach was eventually taken in the late 1970s by combining a dozen or more smaller mirrors into a larger optical framework. This has led to the current Gran Telescopio Canarias whose 36 mirrors provide an aperture with a 10.4 m diameter.

Another technique heavily used in astronomy is called interferometry. By combining the light or radio signals from a source viewed from two telescopes separated by D-metres, you can create a telescope with an effective diameter of D-metres and greatly improve the resolving power of the telescope. Interferometer-based telescopes can now discern details as small as 0.001 arcseconds at radio wavelengths rivalling only the largest optical telescopes. The Very Large Array radio telescope in New Mexico consists of 26 dishes over a baseline some 36 km (22¼ miles) across and can resolve details as small as 0.043 arcseconds.

The VLA interferometer array in New Mexico combines the signals from 26 radio telescopes to create a telescope with very high resolution, which allows photographic-quality radio images to be created of distant nebulae and galaxies.

Meanwhile, some transcontinental Very Long Baseline Interferometry (VLBI) projects involve dozens of individual radio observatories and can achieve a resolution of 10 microarcseconds (0.00001") at a wavelength of 1.3 mm. Provided the source emits enough energy at these wavelengths, near-photographic images can be created of objects buried deep inside obscuring clouds, or of optically invisible plasma ejected from the cores of distant quasars.

The infrared part of the EM was explored in earnest once sensitive 'heat' detectors capable of producing images were developed beginning in the late 1960s. A breakthrough came in 1983 with the advent of the Infrared Astronomical Satellite (IRAS) developed by the European Space Agency with international cooperation. This satellite used sensitive heat sensors, and scanned them across the sky to building up maps of the entire sky at four wavelengths, 12, 25, 60 and 100-microns, revealing a complex universe of multiple sources. The Spitzer Space Telescope launched by NASA in 2003 now gives photographic-quality infrared images of a variety of galaxies and star-forming regions. When combined with radio and optical images of the same source, a truly multi-wavelength perspective can be achieved that reveals the mechanisms behind various phenomena such as star formation and supermassive black hole interactions.

The hidden, dusty arm in NGC 1291 is revealed by the Spitzer Space Telescope, which detects and images infrared radiation from warm dust grains in interstellar clouds.

At shorter wavelengths, we encounter the X-ray universe, which was first discovered in the late 1940's during rocket launches by an astronomer from the Naval Research Laboratory, Ricardo Giacconi. Interest in this important band continued through the 1960s until the launch of the Einstein X-ray Observatory (HEAO-2) in 1978. This complex instrument was eventually superseded by the Chandra X-ray Observatory launched in 1999. Together, they provided high-resolution images of very energetic celestial sources such as supernova remnants, pulsars, black holes and active galaxies. They also discovered for the first time that infant stars are strong sources of X-ray energy.

Gamma-ray telescopes are little more than 1000 kg (2204 lb) boxes of lead with particle detectors at their cores, which look out at the sky along the unshielded 'windows'. The Compton Gamma Ray

The Chandra Observatory, which detects X-ray radiation, reveals jets of matter leaving the pulsar at the center of the Crab supernova remnant.

Observatory launched in 1991 returned a spectacular 'image' of the sky in which daily bursts of energy arrived from distant universe sources more than a billion light years away. These gamma-ray bursts (GRBs) remain an active area of investigation today.

NON-ELECTROMAGNETIC DETECTORS

In addition to the EM radiation carried by photons, other kinds of information messengers criss-cross the universe with their own stories to tell about the nature of cosmic sources.

Neutrinos

Neutrinos are elementary particles with masses over 500,000 times less than an electron, which travel at nearly the speed of light. Across the universe they are generated in the cores of all stars, and also form a relict background radiation left over from the Big Bang itself. The interior of the sun is the strongest local source of neutrinos. With detectors such as the SuperKamiokande Neutrino Observatory in Japan, an enormous tank of sensitive light detectors (photomultiplier tubes) detects the brief flash of a neutrino streaming through the tank. Its direction is noted, and over time a number of these detections build up a very low resolution image of the sky. The solar nuclear furnace shines brightly as a neutrino 'star', which conclusively proved that nuclear fusion is occurring at the core of the sun at the levels predicted by theories of stellar structure and evolution.

Gravitational Radiation

Since Albert Einstein first proposed that gravity waves would spread out from any gravitating object under acceleration, physicists and astronomers have attempted to develop many technologies to detect the changes in the local geometry of space that result from a gravity wave passing close by Earth. The most promising was the interferometer-based coincidence detector. Two beams of laser light would be reflected down an evacuated pipe many kilometres long on two axes 90 degrees apart. The passing gravity wave would imperceptibly change these distances, causing the combined beams to show an interference effect. When two of these 'observatories' are placed thousands of kilometres apart, the coincidence in time of the exact signals will indicate a planet-wide gravity wave effect has been detected. The two Laser Interferometry Gravity Observatory (LIGO) detectors, one in Hanford, Washington and one in Livingston, Louisiana, have now detected ten such bursts since 2015. This not only confirmed a 100-year-old prediction by Einstein, but opened a window on studying black hole and neutron star collisions billions of light years from Earth.

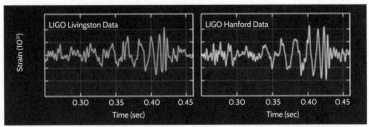

This pulse of gravity waves was detected in 2015 by the LIGO observatories at Livingston and Hanford, and reveals the distortion of spacetime near Earth produced by the collision and merger of two black holes with masses of 29 and 36 Msun.

Photography

Sketches remained the illustrative currency of astronomy books as late as Charles Young's *The Elements of Astronomy* published in 1892. What was needed was a better true-to-life means for capturing an object's actual appearance without a human being part of the equation at all. The advent of photography in the 1800s was the solution. The technique was applied for the first time to astronomical photography in 1840 by John William Draper who 'Daguerrotyped' the full moon, and then in 1845 by Louis Fizeau, who took the first detailed photo of the sun showing sunspots.

One of the first pictures ever taken of the sun, by Leon Foucault and Louis Fizeau in 1845.

There were many improvements in photographic technology that accelerated during the first half of the 20th century in the quest for faster speeds, shorter exposures, and simpler developing techniques. A major stimulus to advancing this technology came from military applications and from the fledgling NASA space programme. In 1965, NASA's Mariner 4 spacecraft flew by Mars and captured a few dozen images of its cratered landscape. It used a scanning video tube whose analogue light intensity output was 'digitized' into a string of numbers and telemetered back to Earth for reconstruction into an image. Then in 1976, astronomers James Janesick and Gerald Smith at the NASA Jet Propulsion Laboratory and the University of Arizona obtained images of Jupiter, Saturn and Uranus using an electronic imaging system called a charge-coupled device or CCD. By 1979, the Kitt Peak National Observatory had mounted a 320×512 pixel digital camera on their 1 m (3¼ ft) telescope and quickly demonstrated the superiority of CCDs over photographic plates. By the 1990s, the Hubble Space Telescope used several imaging arrays including the 4096×4096 WFPC-3 camera (16 megapixels).

The galaxy Messier 101 viewed by the Hubble Space Telescope reveals complex nebulae and star-forming regions as well as individual stars.

Ground-based leviathans such as the Large Synoptic Survey Telescope use arrays of 3200 megapixels. By comparison, common smartphone camera systems available since 2008 have 16 megapixel arrays, but of far lower quality than astronomical imagers of the same size.

As telescopes became more powerful it became necessary to develop instrumentation to make full use of the information they were providing. Astronomers developed devices to measure the positions of stars accurately, to gauge their light intensity and analyse their spectral properties. These can be represented by the terms micrometry, photometry and spectroscopy.

Micrometry

Astronomers realized that some stars form binary pairs that travel through space. This led to the idea of placing a measurement device at the eyepiece that could record the positions of stars over months and years. Numerous micrometer designs were employed in the 16th and 17th centuries. Filar micrometers were designed

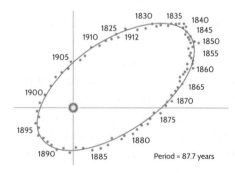

The star 70 Ophiuchus A is a binary star. These micrometer measurements from 1825 to 1910 show the motion of the companion star 70 Ophiuchus B spanning 90 years with the main star located at the centre.

so that through the eyepiece, the astronomer could place one measuring 'fibre' on the east–west location of a star and a second fibre could be moved along the north–south direction. The co-ordinates of the primary and secondary stars could then be recorded to fractions of an arcsecond accuracy to determine the orbit of the secondary star.

Spectroscopy

Beginning with the advent of laboratory spectroscopy in the mid-1800s, astronomers soon adapted this technology to determine the element compositions of the sun, planets, stars, nebulae and galaxies over the course of the next century. Photographic techniques were used by Harvard astronomers Annie Jump Cannon and Howard Pickering to classify hundreds of spectra simultaneously using a simple prismatic 'wedge' fitted over the aperture of the telescope to disperse the starlight. Also by this time, George Ellery Hale had discovered in 1895 that if you used the spectroscope as a filter, you could scan the exiting light from individual spectral lines and build up an image of the sun at specific wavelengths. This ushered in spectroheliometry, which is widely

The Great Telescope of the Lick Observatory built in 1888 with an aperture of 91 mm (36 inches) located at Mt Hamilton, California. After considerable upgrades in technology, it is still in operation today.

used today, not just for studying solar activity, but to examine the multi-wavelength properties of nebulae and galaxies. These spectro-photographic technologies grew in importance during the 1920s as astronomers Vesto Slipher and Edwin Hubble turned their attentions towards faint galaxies and discovered the expansion of the universe.

The simultaneous measurement of the light from hundreds of galaxies at a time can now be accomplished with the help of fibre optics. In a multi-fibre spectrometer, a metal plate fits on the focal plane of the telescope and is drilled with hundreds of holes. Each hole is centred on a particular galaxy to be imaged at a particular sky location. Into each hole, a single fibre optic cable is attached. The light from the galaxy is carried to the spectrometer and becomes its own spectrum of light. Over one hundred galaxies each hour can be analysed in this way and their doppler shifts determined by a computer program.

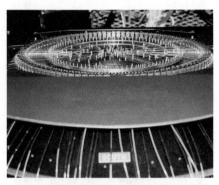

The Hydra Multi-Fiber Spectrograph at Kitt Peak National Observatory. Each fibre optic cable feeds the light from a single galaxy to the main spectrograph so that hundreds of galaxy spectra can be photographed at the same time.

An important feature of spectroscopes is their ability to disperse light with a high enough range so that very narrow-wavelength spectral features can be discerned. The resolution of a spectroscope is defined as $R = \lambda/\Delta\lambda$. This means for the $\lambda=6563$ Angstroms hydrogen-alpha line, it can be resolved with a spectroscope with a resolution of $R = 110,000$ so that features as small as $\Delta\lambda=0.06$ Angstroms can be seen. For Doppler shift studies, this means that the instrument can also resolve speed differences of $V = c \times 1/R$ where c is the speed of light and so $\Delta V = 3$ km/sec.

Photometers

Like the light meter in your camera, a photometer is a sensitive instrument that can measure the brightness of stars and other astronomical objects with great precision. Photometry first came into use by the Greek astronomer Hipparchus in 150BCE, who classified the stars into six magnitudes using their apparent brightness to the human eye. One 'magnitude' corresponds to a brightness change by a factor of 2.512 or $100^{1/5}$, and careful and skilled astronomers could estimate star brightness to a precision of about 0.1 magnitudes on this scale. A major advance in star brightness measurement did not happen until the second half of the 19th century, when Friedrich Zollner devised the kerosene reference lamp which would be compared to a star's brightness by varying a polarizing filter to match the star's brightness. Measurements accurate to 0.05 magnitudes could now be made. Eventually, photographic techniques were used to make brightness measurements, which by the 1930s gave accuracies near 0.02 magnitudes. One of the most exciting applications of these technologies is in the detection of planets orbiting distant stars.

Just as a star exerts a gravitational pull on orbiting planets, an orbiting planet exerts a relatively small pull on its star. When viewed spectroscopically, this wobble is seen as a slight Doppler redshift in the line-of-sight *radial velocity* of the star as it moves away from the viewer, and a slight Doppler blueshift as it moves towards the viewer. This speed shift can be measured and amounts to a few metres per second (m/s) change that would be periodic in time as

The German astrophysicist Friedrich Zollner (1834-1882) devised a method of measuring a star's brightness using a kerosene lamp and a polarizing filter.

the planet orbited the star. Radial velocity can also determine a planet's mass and, in conjunction with its orbital period, this can determine whether it is a rocky or gaseous planet.

The slight wobble in a star's orbit can be measured with respect to the background stars, known as *proper motion*. The amount of movement is a small fraction of a second of arc (1/3600 of a degree). The Keck telescopes in Hawaii have astrometrical devices that can measure such movement in stars to an accuracy of 20 micro arcseconds.

If the line of sight to the star is exactly in the orbit plane of the planet, as the planet orbits the star it passes across the disk of the star, called a *transit*, causing a slight (around 1 per cent) change in the star's brightness. Precision photometers can measure this slight light change in great detail and discern the size and even the shape of the planet. By measuring the spectra of the starlight as the planet passes in front of its star, astronomers can spectroscopically analyse the planet's atmosphere and identify its chemical constituents.

Telescopes are becoming powerful enough to view exoplanets directly. The main problem this *direct imaging* technique faces is in blocking the glare from the star so that the light reflected from orbiting exoplanets can be detected. The two main ways to do this are to use a device to block the star's light before it enters the telescope (known as a *star shade*), or to mask the star inside the telescope before its light can reach the detector (known as *coronagraphy*). As this technique improves, it should be possible to analyse the planet's atmosphere and surface properties.

The light from a more distant star can steadily brighten as an exoplanet orbiting a foreground star passes in front of it. Through a process called *gravitational lensing*, its gravity focuses and bends the light from the background star. If the nearer star has an orbiting planet there will be a momentary increase in light from the more distant star as the planet's gravity is added to that of its star. This method has also been used to detect and study faint galaxies in the distant universe using the lensing properties of foreground clusters of galaxies.

Key Points

- Telescopes are instruments that collect electro-magnetic radiation using mirrors, lenses or even solid blocks of matter and amplify weak signals from distant objects so that they can be detected.

- For telescopes that operate from ultraviolet to radio wavelengths, the area of the aperture relates to the amplification of the weak signal by collecting more photons of light. The resolution of the telescope and its ability to resolve minute details is proportional to the wavelength and inversely proportional to its aperture diameter.

- The most important astronomical instrument has been the spectroscope, which lets astronomers discover the chemical composition and doppler speeds of celestial objects such as planets, nebulae and galaxies.

- The advent of photography in the 1800s freed astronomers from having to sketch what they saw at the eyepiece, which is a method fraught with human error.

- Photography lets a telescope accumulate small numbers of photons from faint objects over extended periods of time to build up a clear image.

Chapter 2

Measuring the Universe

Astronomy has always been an observational, data-driven science. Precise measurement of the distance between stars, planets and galaxies is an important, but often challenging task. Over the centuries, astronomers have developed a number of techniques to determine distances and to categorize stars and new units to make sense of measurements on a galactic scale.

RIGHT ASCENSION AND DECLINATION

The location of a star in the sky is determined by its address in the Right Ascension (RA) and Declination (Dec.) coordinate system, which operates like longitude and latitude on Earth. The Dec. coordinate works like latitude with the north celestial pole at +90.0° and the south celestial pole at -90.0°. This degree measure is in turn broken down into arcminutes, which are 1/60 of an angular degree, and arcseconds which are 1/60 of an arcminute. Because the earth rotates, the apparent RA of a star changes continuously so it is convenient to measure a star's angular position in RA in terms of hours, minutes and seconds such that 1 hour in RA is equal to 15°. The angular distance between two stars in the sky can be determined by converting their RA into angular degrees, and then using the appropriate spherical trigonometry formula to calculate this separation angle. Early star catalogues only cited star positions to an accuracy of 1/10 of a degree, but modern catalogues specify positions to 0.001 arcseconds or better.

PARALLAX

Parallax is an angle measured in degrees that obtains when you view an object of a fixed diameter (in metres) or separation, from a distance (also in metres). This effect can also be reversed so that if you measure the parallax angle with a theodolite, and know beforehand the size of the distant object in metres, you can determine its distance also in metres. The basic formula is

$$Parallax\ angle = 57.3\ \frac{Displacement\ (m)}{Distance\ (m)}\ degrees$$

Hipparchus pioneered the method of parallax to gauge the distance to the moon, but when parallax or other methods based upon lunar phases (Aristarchus) were applied to the earth-sun distance (called the Astronomical Unit or AU), the results were inaccurate by factors of a thousand. Ptolemy's estimate of 1200 earth radii or about 7 million km (4 million miles) remained the gold standard for the AU until the time of Copernicus. A much more precise value was finally determined using telescopic techniques by Jean Richer and Giovanni Cassini. They measured the parallax of Mars between Paris and Cayenne in French Guiana when Mars was at its closest to Earth in 1672. From their measured parallax angle, and the predicted distance to Mars based on Kepler's AU scale for planetary distances, they deduced that 1

Giovanni Cassini (also known as Jean-Dominique Cassini), with the help of Jean Richer, measured the distance between Earth and Mars.

AU corresponded to a distance of 21,700 earth radii or 140 million km (87 million miles). The adopted modern value for the AU is 149 million km.

Stars are even farther away than the planets, but the distances to the nearest ones can also be determined using the parallax technique. However, in this case the baseline used for gauging the angles is not the distance between your eyes, but the distance between Earth in space from its orbit 6 months apart. From this 2 AU baseline, photographs, or careful micrometre measurements, of the position of a star against more distant background stars shows a periodic 6-month motion such that at a distance of 1 parsec or 206265 AU, the shift in the star's position is exactly 1 arcsecond of 1/3600 of an angular degree. The parsec is one fundamental measure of astronomical distances and it is related to the light-year such that 1 parsec equals 3.26 light years. A light year is the distance light travels in one Earth year or 9.5 trillion km (6 trillion miles).

SCIENTIFIC NOTATION

The dimensions of mass, distance and luminosity of astronomical objects are so vast that we must use a new system of representing these numbers involving what is called scientific notation. The gist of this notation is that a number is represented as a decimal number between 0 and 9.9999 followed by a power-of-ten multiplier. For example, the number 1,350,000 can be stated as 1.35 million and written as 1.35×10^6. The number 0.0054 can be stated as 5.4 thousandths, or as 5.4×10^{-3}. Writing large numbers in this way allows for simple multiplication and division when needed by following the usual laws of multiplying numbers and adding (for multiplication) or subtracting (for division) exponents.

Another arena in which astronomers use slightly different scales than those we normally use day-to-day is in the measure of temperature. Whether you are familiar with the Fahrenheit or Celsius conventions, these can be related to a physically more fundamental scale called the Kelvin scale. Unlike C and F, which are stated in terms of degree units, the Kelvin scale begins at Absolute Zero, which is assigned an exact numeric value of 0.0. Because this represents the condition of exactly zero motion and energy, there are no negative Kelvin values, only positive ones. The kelvin unit is a pure number with no units, and temperature measurements are represented as for instance 5,770K, and not 5,770°K. However, the Kelvin scale can be directly related to the Celsius scale in which the freezing point of pure water is at 0°C and 273.15K, and a 1K temperature difference equals 1°C.

ASTRONOMICAL CATALOGUES

The most ancient star catalogue that has survived to the present time is the 'Three Stars Each' list of the Babylonians ca 1200BCE, which consisted of nothing more than the lists of the three brightest stars in each of the twelve zodiacal houses. After 350BCE, Timocharis, Aristarchus, Aristillus, Archimedes, Hipparchus and the Chinese astrologer Shi Shen can be counted among the first individuals to have used the degree measure, by dividing the circle into 360 degrees, with each degree consisting of 60 arc minutes. During the 1700s and 1800s, many astronomers developed extensive star catalogues with accurate star positions to fractions of an arcsecond. By the mid-1800s, the Bonner Durchmusterung catalogue totalled some 320,000 stars. In 1885, Edward Pickering at the Harvard College Observatory undertook an ambitious program of stellar spectral classification using 10,000 spectra recorded on photographic plates. Following Pickering's vision, Annie Jump Cannon expanded the 'Henry Draper' catalogue to nine volumes and over a quarter of a million stars by 1924, and developed a system of seven spectral types – O, B, A, F, G, K, M – that astronomers quickly accepted for world-wide use.

Cecilia Payne (1900–79) later used this data to study the atmospheres of stars. Payne won a scholarship in 1919 to Newnham College, Cambridge University, where she read botany, physics, and chemistry. At Harvard, under the direction of Harlow Shapley, she wrote her 1925 doctor's dissertation on 'Stellar Atmospheres'.

ANNIE JUMP CANNON

Annie Jump Cannon (1863–1941) was an American astronomer whose cataloguing work played a major role in how stars are classified today. Edward Pickering hired her at the Harvard College Observatory as an assistant in 1896. Her effort involved classifying the spectra of over 350,000 stars. Astronomers were previously using a 22-type alphabetic scheme, but after finding duplicates this was reduced to a smaller series and rearranged by Canon to reflect a temperature order, giving us the modern O, B, A, F, G, K, M system. She was admitted into the Royal Astronomical Society in 1914, and was the first woman to be given an honorary doctorate at Oxford in 1925.

Annie Jump Cannon developed the O, B, A, F, G, K, M system of categorizing stars.

She used Annie Jump Canon's stellar classification data, along with the newly developed theory of quantum mechanics, to prove among other things that stars were made mostly of hydrogen and helium. Astronomer Otto Struve called it 'undoubtedly the most brilliant Ph.D thesis ever written in astronomy'.

During the late 1900s, several newer star catalogues such as the US Naval Observatory B1.0 catalogue include positions for over one billion stars and galaxies, are complete to a visual magnitude of +21^m, and have a positional accuracy of 0.2 arcseconds. Two massive catalogues were created from specialized satellite data beginning with the Hipparcos Catalogue ca 1989 containing 120,000 stars with positions accurate to 0.001 arcseconds, and the Gaia Catalogue ca 2016 with over one billion stars with positions accurate to 0.0007 arcseconds or better for stars brighter than $+21^m$.

In 1771, comet hunter Charles Messier began to publish a list of fuzzy non-stellar objects that should not be mistaken for comets. This list of 'Messier Objects' led to a catalogue of some 110 entries that we now recognize as star clusters and nebulae, along with a number of galaxies beyond the Milky Way. In 1786, William Herschel, and later his wife Caroline and son John, compiled a catalogue of over 2000 objects fainter than what Messier had found. By 1888, John Dreyer used the Herschel catalogue and other collected observations to create the *New General Catalogue*, which is the standard reference source for modern astronomers in citing the brighter galaxies in research papers according to an 'NGC' index number. The Messier catalogue is also still used to cite some of the brighter objects in the sky such as the Orion Nebula as M-42, or as NGC-1976.

Galaxies were not randomly sprinkled across the sky but favoured large associations known to 19th-century astronomers as the Virgo and Coma clouds. Among the first systematic catalogues of galaxy clusters was that created by George Abell using the Palomar Observatory Sky

John Dreyer (1852–1924) developed the New General Catalogue which lists galaxies, nebulae and other phenomena in space and is still widely used by astronomers today.

Survey photographs developed in the late 1940s. Over 2,700 'Abell Clusters' were identified by 1958, and this catalogue was extended to include an additional 1,361 clusters in the southern hemisphere in 1989. A variety of modern galaxy catalogues includes the Sloan Digital Sky Survey of 2000 with over three million galaxies, as well as specialized catalogues of hundreds of thousands of quasars and other peculiar extragalactic objects.

COMPUTING TECHNOLOGY

By the time of Newton, the mathematical description of planetary motion was rapidly outstripping our ability to hand-calculate the predictions hidden within the complex mathematical equations. Vast quantities of quill-and-ink calculations had to be performed to reach even the simplest predictions. Luckily, this last constraint on the practical uses of mathematics in astronomy was also beginning to fall.

Between Blaise Pascal's 1642 mechanical calculator for addition and subtraction and the first commercial calculator, the Arithmometer offered in 1851 by Thomas de Colmar, astronomers made do with combinations of long-hand and calculator-assisted work. The Arithmometer made possible the multiplication of two 8-digit numbers in only 18 seconds, so improving the speed of calculations was already seen as a desirable goal by the mid-1800s. Calculating planetary orbits was the chief, and very time-consuming, occupation of many astronomers for predicting where planets should appear in the sky at any time of the day, and the occurrence and circumstances of lunar and solar eclipses. The first official *American Ephemeris and Nautical Almanac* was published in 1852, but the British *Nautical Almanac and Astronomical Ephemeris* had been published each year since 1766. The demanding and detailed calculations to make the following year's predictions had to be performed in less than a year in order to make the production and printing deadlines for the next *Ephemeris* year. Legions of human 'computers' worked behind the scenes to make this happen.

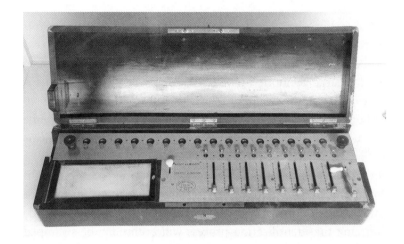

The Arithmometer was the first commercial calculator in ca 1866. It was capable of multiplying two 8-digit numbers in 18 seconds.

As computation technology evolved, so did the accuracy and 'resolution' of the forecasts, largely based upon Newtonian physics and improved astronomical data made with sophisticated, high-precision telescopes. This progress was dramatically improved with the advent of computers one hundred years later, so that today, calculations of complex mathematical models from climate change to stellar evolution are performed on supercomputers capable of trillions of operations every second.

A cosmologist using a supercomputer at the University of Durham known as the 'Cosmology Machine'.

33

A major challenge for astronomers in the 21st century is working with huge databases generated by photographic surveys and other specialized imaging projects. Modern telescopes such as the Large Synoptic Survey Telescope will generate 15 terabytes of data every night and provide information for nearly 40 billion stars and galaxies. It is impossible for humans to handle this amount of data, so new techniques involving Artificial Intelligence are being developed to identify the many millions of interesting objects that change position or brightness from night to night. Currently, citizen scientists have been used to look for interesting and novel features in imaging data, but even crowd-sourcing the identification process will eventually be swamped by the sheer volume of data generated every day, so new 'machine processing' and pattern recognition techniques involving AI will eventually have to be used.

Astronomers since the dawn of the Space Age in the 1960s have relied on instruments and telescopes launched into space to study individual planets, moons and asteroids as well as the sun and the distant stars. Some types of data cannot be acquired from the surface of Earth with large telescopes so spacecraft are designed to make these observations from space, or by orbiting the object of interest (e.g. moon, Mars and Venus) and making the observations in situ. Currently, rovers on Mars such as Curiosity are providing geologic and atmospheric measurements of surface conditions, while spacecraft such as the Solar Dynamics Observatory and the Hubble Space Telescope return terabytes of imaging data every year of the solar surface and deep space objects across the universe.

Key Points

- Astronomers use angular measures to locate objects in the sky in terms of the Right Ascension and Declination co-ordinate system.

- An Astronomical Unit is the distance from Earth to the Sun and is equal to 149 million kilometres, and one light year is equal to 9.5 trillion kilometres (6 trillion miles).

- Astronomers create extensive catalogues of objects in the sky to keep track of their properties and movements.

- Computers are invaluable tools for performing complex and time-consuming calculations needed for developing catalogues, designing telescopes and mathematically modelling astronomical phenomena.

- The parallax technique is one of the most basic means for determining the distances to objects in the solar system and many nearby stars.

Chapter 3

Mathematics and Theories

There has never been a time when mathematics has not been an integral part of the human process of understanding the cosmos, whether it is the arithmetic Venus-sighting calculations of the ancient Babylonians, or the intricate geometric designs by ancient Greek astronomers such as Ptolemy. Astronomy has always been an observational, data-driven science, and for quantitative data in numerical form, there is no better way to organize it and extract meaning from it than through logical and mathematical manipulation.

The dramatic increase in measurement capability provided

by Tycho Brahe led to much higher quality data, and it was no longer adequate to model planetary orbits as concentric circles. By the early 1600s, Johannes Kepler's First Law derived from the new data was that planets orbit the sun on

Johannes Kepler discovered three laws of planetary motion which have proved essential to our understanding of astronomy.

elliptical orbits. His 'Third Law of Planetary Motion', stated as the period-squared is proportional to the distance-cubed or $T^2 = A^3$, also required an algebraic approach to analysing the data rather than a more cumbersome geometric one.

NEWTON AND GRAVITY

The next major change in how astronomers worked with astronomical data and its mathematical modelling occurred almost single-handedly at the hands of Sir Isaac Newton in 1666. Newton, working with the ideas developed for mass, velocity, acceleration and force by Galileo Galilei in the 1640s, took these ideas and developed a detailed mathematical framework for motion under the influence of his Universal Law of Gravity stated simply as

$$F = \frac{GMm}{d^2}$$

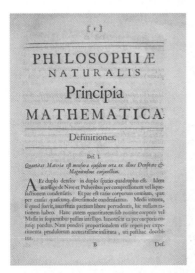

Isaac Newton's Principia Mathematica *is one of the most important books on mathematics ever written and had a particular influence on astrophysics.*

His book *Principia,* published in 1687, is considered one of the greatest mathematical *tours de force* in physics, laying out many new laws and principles in algebraic fashion. In it, he not only described how gravity operates but discussed and calculated tidal influences and planetary orbits, the precession of the Equinoxes and the orbit of the moon and invented a whole new form of mathematics we now call the calculus, or as Newton called it 'The Method of Fluxions'. Later in 1680, Robert Hooke mentioned to Newton that he believed without proof that the inverse-square law for gravity led to elliptical planetary orbits. The inverse-square law in optics describes how the brightness, B, of an object decreases as the distance to the observer, d, increases according to the simple formula

$$B = \frac{I}{d^2}$$

so that if you double the distance, the brightness decreases by a factor of 4. Newton showed that the same diminution law also applies to gravity. Newton took Hooke's proposal as a challenge and quickly proved this basic fact as a natural result of his Law of Gravity acting between the planet and the sun.

The transition from simple algebra being used by Kepler to formulate the laws of planetary motion, to Newton's deep-dive into mathematics to account for the detailed motions of bodies under the influence of gravity, set the stage for many more centuries of merging mathematics with expositions of why things happen the way that they do. Mathematics increasingly provided a new 'telescope' with which astronomers could understand seemingly implacable discoveries made through their telescopes and instruments. Eugene Wigner in 1960 would go on to write an article 'The Unreasonable Effectiveness of Mathematics in the Natural Sciences' where he concludes 'the miracle of the appropriateness of the language of mathematics for the formulation of the

Sir Isaac Newton, the developer of modern mathematical techniques in physics including the Law of Universal Gravitation.

laws of physics is a wonderful gift which we neither understand nor deserve'.

EINSTEIN AND RELATIVITY

Albert Einstein's development of the Special and General Theory of Relativity in 1905 and 1915 led to the Relativity Revolution and the idea that time and space are intertwined as a single object, a phenomenon called by the mathematician Hermann Minkowski 'spacetime'. This four-dimensional object had three dimensions we call space and one dimension we call time, but integrated together so that every observer in the universe sees them as a single mathematical object. Among the central discoveries of relativity is that matter and energy are equivalent ways of describing the same things, and this is codified in Einstein's iconic equation $E=mc^2$. This simple idea allowed astronomers to eventually discover that stars obtain their luminous energy through the fusion of hydrogen nuclei, which causes millions of tons of matter in a star to be transformed into pure energy every second.

Einstein's general relativity also offered the first mathematical treatment of the origin and evolution of the universe, which later predicted the expansion of the universe discovered by Edwin Hubble as the Hubble Law, which is stated as $V = Hd$. Also, Einstein's relativistic version of gravity led to the prediction of the existence of black holes in which matter is hidden from view by a region of space called the event horizon that extends a distance of $R = 2.89$ M kilometres from an object with a mass of M times the mass of our sun.

THEORIES BASED ON OBSERVATION

In addition to the various mathematical theories of space and time provided by relativity, physicists had been developing in parallel detailed, observation-based theories of the nature of matter and energy beginning with James Clerk Maxwell's Theory of Electrodynamics in the 1800s, and leading to the advent of quantum mechanics in the 1920s. It was now possible to understand the nature of matter and its interaction with light in enough detail to account for the spectroscopic data acquired by astronomers in their studies of stars and galaxies. This symbiotic relationship between astronomy and physics, astrophysics, has now led to detailed mathematical models of the evolution of stars, the formation of dense objects such as neutron stars and black holes, and a whole host of other astronomical phenomena. In fact, no matter where modern physics goes in its detailed analysis of the forces and elementary particles of nature called the Standard Model, there is always an astronomical system that benefits from the new knowledge. For example, one of the most complex areas of research is called quantum field theory in which the unification of the forces of nature including gravity is being pursued. However, the lessons being learned from this highly mathematical subject are shining a powerful light onto the most sublime question in all of astronomy: 'How did the universe, itself, come into existence?'

What the combination of quantitative mathematical theories and lightning-fast calculation using computers has allowed us to do is to experience many natural phenomena by greatly slowing down their speeds for atomic systems, or speeding them up for astronomical systems. The accuracy of modern explanations for how things work now rests on making accurate calculations directed by powerful mathematically-stated theories without having to make any approximations, then using supercomputers to render the theoretical prediction into quantities that can be measured. We can test the accuracy of Big Bang cosmology with dark matter and dark energy added, by using our theories to describe how Standard Model matter will interact, and follow the evolution of structure in the universe over cosmological times. The prediction of what the current structure should be like in all of its galactic detail can be compared with what astronomers actually see across the universe today to test the underlying theories. When major 'new physics' has been left out, the result is usually a big difference between what the astronomer sees in their data and what the mathematical model predicts. Similarly, the detonation of a supernova and the formation of neutron stars and black holes can be modelled theoretically. The supercomputer calculations then let astronomers slow down the evolution of this process, which takes a few hours so that it can be explored from millisecond to millisecond.

Result of a supercomputer Millennium Simulation of cosmic structure at a scale of 100 million light years across. Each dot represents an individual galaxy, and the model is based upon Newton's law of gravity operating between galaxies on the cosmological scale.

MODERN ASTROPHYSICS

Astrophysics in the 21st century has now evolved dramatically from even its mid-1900s roots, while at the same time confronted by challenges that could not have been pursued by anything less than the technology and techniques that have been amassed since the turn of the millennium. Modern astronomers are still intimately involved in the development and articulation of physical theories of specific objects and the universe at large, but now theories may be tested against data with a level of detail that forces theories to accurately predict physical outcomes at higher and higher resolution. Studies of supernova detonations and black hole mergers could at one time be advanced by simple 'back of the envelope' calculations performed on table-top computers. Today, supercomputers reveal near-photographic changes in these systems at time scales of milliseconds.

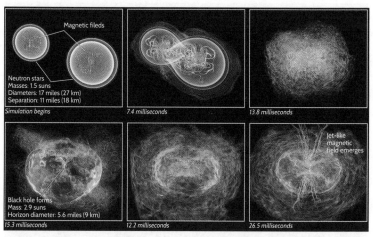

Simulation of colliding neutron stars spanning 27 milliseconds. Each neutron star has about the same mass as our sun but with a diameter of only 50 kilometres (31 miles). Einstein's theory of general relativity must be used to accurately describe the motions due to the enormous strength of gravity on these scales.

Thanks to the synthesis of mathematics, supercomputer modelling and advanced imaging technology, astrophysics in the 21st century is a far richer and more exciting undertaking than any previous generations of astronomers could ever have imagined. At the end of the day, there are always more mysteries to contemplate, with the prospect of uncovering signs of an even more sublime and inventive universe in the decades to come.

Key Points

- Because data is in the form of numbers, mathematics is the only natural language for data analysis that helps astronomers extract patterns and consistent natural laws from an onslaught of numerical information.

- Many different forms of mathematics are used, with statistics being crucial for understanding the measurement process and discerning correlations in the measurement.

- Our detailed understanding of the universe comes about because with mathematics we can investigate and propose higher-order relationships among the correlations we find in the data. These become entire schemes of understanding such as quantum mechanics, electrodynamics, relativity and cosmology.

- Computers have evolved over the last 50 years into mathematical tools for analysing huge amounts of data and converting mathematical models into concrete predictions of what to look for next.

- Supercomputers are now so powerful that they can follow billions of points of matter in the expanding universe to study the evolution of structure and galaxies spanning billions of years.

PART II
The Sun

Chapter 4

Solar Structure

The Sun has been studied since ancient times. Chinese astrologers would carefully track spots on the Sun and use them for making forecasts for the Emperor. The English astronomer Thomas Harriot was the first to record seeing sunspots using a telescope, in 1610, viewing the Sun on a misty day to reduce the glare. But he shared his findings with only a few close associates. Other astronomers, including Galileo Galilei, David Fabricius and Christoph Scheiner, made the same discovery the following year. Like Harriot, Fabricius tracked them as the Sun rotated. Sunspots quickly entered mainstream science and, in 1843, astronomer Samuel Heinrich Schwabe discovered that the number of sunspots followed an 11-year rise and fall in numbers, which came to be known as the *sunspot cycle*.

By the 1800s, studies of total solar eclipses had demonstrated that the solar disk was surrounded by an atmosphere called the *corona* that could extend several times the diameter of the Sun into space. Extensive, and some very beautiful, sketches and paintings of the corona became commonplace. The first solar photograph was captured by Johann Julius Friedrich Berkowski during the total solar eclipse of 28 July 1851.

In 1856, Edward Sabine made the connection between sunspot activity and auroral activity – the 'Northern Lights' (*aurora borealis*). Since the correlations between aurora and geomagnetic storms had been discovered by Anders Celsius and Olof Hiorter in 1741, some scientists such as Kristian Birkeland in 1898 claimed that sunspots were magnetic phenomena that emitted a ray of particles towards Earth. This idea was dismissed by Lord Kelvin, who argued that magnetism could not travel the great distances between the Sun and Earth without huge attenuation in strength.

The advent of spectroscopy (see page 21) in the mid-1800s opened up a window to exploring the composition of the Sun, and later its magnetism and rotation. The first discovery was that sunlight contained the absorption line signatures of many different elements, including one never seen on Earth: helium. During the solar eclipse of 7 August 1869, astronomers Charles Young and William Harkness discovered a mysterious spectral line in the solar corona with a wavelength of 530.3 nm. It wasn't until 1930 that physicists Walter Grotrain and Bengt Edlen identified it as emission from an iron atom ionized 13 times. It requires temperatures in excess of a few million degrees to strip iron atoms of so many electrons.

The Sun, as a gaseous sphere, rotates once every 25.6 days at the equator and 33.5 days at the poles. It is classified as a G2 dwarf star with surface temperature of 5,770 K, a mass of 1.9×10^{30} kg and a luminosity of 4.0×10^{26} watts/m^2. The Sun's lumi-

Kristian Birkeland originated the idea that sunspots were magnetic disturbances on the Sun that caused the aurora borealis on Earth.

nosity makes it brighter than about 85 per cent of all stars in the Milky Way, but fainter stars are far more common by factors of fifty or more. The Sun is composed of 74.9 per cent hydrogen and 23.8 per cent helium, with all the other elements in the periodic table accounting for the remaining two per cent – often called the 'heavy elements'.

The nature of the process responsible for the Sun's luminosity was of considerable interest throughout the 19th century when chemical combustion and gravitational energy were the only energy sources known. Hermann von Helmholtz's 1854 proposal that the Sun's energy came about from its slow gravitational collapse was a more plausible process than chemical combustion, but even this mechanism had its problems. Lord Kelvin used this new mechanism to estimate the age of the Sun, but achieved estimates of only about 30 million years. This turned out to be in conflict with the Earth's geological age of at least 100 million years deduced from the erosion of mountains and the laying down of sedimentary rocks. The inconsistency was not firmly resolved until the advent of nuclear physics after the 1920s, and in particular the work by Arthur Eddington in the 1920s and Hans Bethe in 1939, working from Albert Einstein's $E = mc^2$ equation. The key mechanism was a process called thermonuclear fusion, which begins with the most abundant material in the Sun: hydrogen. A series of steps that 'burns' hydrogen fuel and releases nuclear energy has come to be known as the Proton–Proton (P–P) reaction. It takes place in stars near the mass of our Sun, which can sustain the necessary core temperatures by gravitational compression and heating to allow the reaction to proceed quickly. A second reaction cycle called the Carbon–Nitrogen–Oxygen (CNO) cycle gradually replaces the P–P cycle for stars more massive than the Sun.

Because of electrostatic repulsion, two protons have to collide at very high energy in order to fuse. An adequate number of these collisions takes place at temperatures in excess of 12 million K. However, a single proton may have to wait millions of years before it is involved in a successful fusion episode because one of

49

The steps in the Proton–Proton fusion reaction leading to an 'ash' of helium nuclei. Helium nuclei fuse to form deuterium (²H), which then fuse to form tritium (³He). Two tritium nuclei then fuse to form a stable helium (⁴He) nucleus plus two hydrogen nuclei. Nuclear energy is released in the form of gamma rays (γ) and kinetic energy.

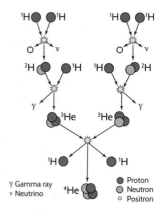

the two protons has to also simultaneously turn into a neutron to form a *deuterium* nucleus (an isotope of hydrogen containing one neutron). Once this bottleneck is passed, the rest of the reactions lead very quickly to the formation of helium ash. The P–P cycle is so efficient that it generates 4×10^{26} watts of solar light energy, as well as keeping the internal plasma hot enough to prevent the gravitational collapse of the Sun within a few hours. Based upon Einstein's $E = mc^2$, a total of 4.3 million metric tons of mass have to be converted into light energy every second. This requires the fusion of 600 megatons of hydrogen every second.

Since the time of Eddington, astrophysicists have developed detailed models of the interior of the Sun based upon temperature, density, state of ionization, plasma motions and other factors that change from the centre of the Sun to the visible surface.

THE CORE

The enormous fusion output of the Sun is confined to the core region where gravitational compression and heating have raised the plasma temperature to over 12 million K. The core occupies about 20 per cent of the solar radius, and has a peak density of 150 gm/cc or nearly that of lead. Once produced, the high-energy photons scatter about from nucleon to nucleon. This partially provides the kinetic 'heat' energy that supplies the internal pressure of the star. However, some of the photons are steadily degraded in energy until they reach the surface, where upon they become the radiant light energy of the Sun. Estimates suggest that it may take tens of thousands of years for a 'single' photon in the core to reach the solar surface.

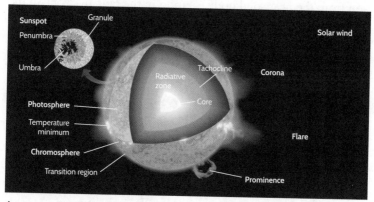

A cross-section of the solar interior showing the principle zones, surface phenomena and the extended solar corona.

THE RADIATIVE REGION

Beyond the core, and extending to about 70 per cent of the solar radius, we reach a new set of thermal and plasma conditions in which the energy generated by the core must travel in the most efficient way possible. Heat always moves from a hotter region to a colder region, so the tremendous flow of energy from the core streams through this plasma region, whose density falls from 20 gm/cc to 0.2 gm/cc while its temperature falls from 7 million K to 2 million K. Technically, because the temperature difference across this region is less than what is called the *adiabatic lapse rate* ($\Delta T/\Delta l$, or the change in gas temperature divided by the distance across which the temperature change occurs), convective motions cannot occur and the plasma appears essentially frozen in space while the photon energy flows through it. From the top of the radiative zone to the centre of the core, the Sun rotates like a nearly solid body with a period of 95 per cent of the equatorial rate or one rotation every 24 days.

THE TACHOCLINE

The *tachocline* is an important region of the Sun only recently recognized by solar physicists. In this very narrow zone perhaps no more than 30,000 km (18,640 miles) thick, there is a sharp transition from the near solid body rotation in the radiative zone to the differential rotation of the overlying convective zone. This results in significant shearing of the plasma, which is thought to generate the solar magnetic field and to control the sunspot cycle itself.

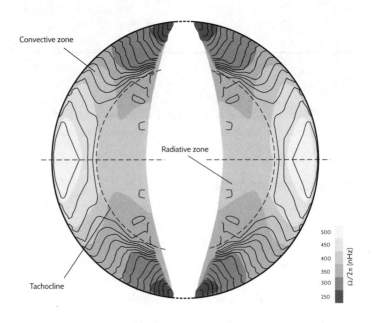

A model of the shearing flows in the solar tachocline shown with a concentric dotted line. Below the tachocline is the calm radiative zone, and above it is the turbulent convective zone. Plasma currents in this region generate the solar magnetic field.

THE CONVECTIVE ZONE

The *convective zone* extends from 72 per cent of the solar radius just above the tachocline to nearly the solar surface itself, which is called the *photosphere*. Plasma in this zone drops in temperature from about 2 million K to the temperature at the solar surface of 5,770 K. The density falls from about 0.2 gm/cc to 0.0001 gm/cc. Together with the dramatic declines in the ionization of the plasma, the temperature and density change across the convection region makes the plasma unstable to convection, which now becomes the most efficient way to transport heat from the solar interior to the surface. Mathematical modelling of this convective process reveals several different scales of convection including supergranular convection with scales at the surface nearly comparable to the depth of the convective zone (30,000 km). Superimposed on these supercells are the normal convective cells seen in the photosphere with sizes of a few thousand km.

THE PHOTOSPHERE

The *photosphere* is the outer layer of the Sun visible from Earth with optical telescopes. Through studies at a variety of wavelengths, it has been known for decades to be exceedingly complex. The complexity of structures and forms is due in large measure to the fact that the outer surface is threaded by magnetic fields. These fields cause a variety of transient phenomena, from slow-changing sunspots to minute-by-minute outbursts called *solar flares*. Magnetic fields often act like pipes carrying charged plasmas great distances above the photosphere in structures called prominences. Gravity and magnetic forces can be in temporary balance allowing prominences to remain stable for many days. When this balance is upset, erupting prominences destabilize and expand outwards into the corona. Meanwhile, surface granulation convects plasma from deeper layers, and at the boundaries of adjacent cells, magnetic fields can concentrate, forming a magnetic network.

Sunspots usually appear in pairs for which one spot has the opposite magnetic polarity of the other. Convection and surface motions can carry sunspots into collision, or cause them to split apart into migrating polar regions, growing into still larger sunspot groups. Also, when the surface motions compress opposing

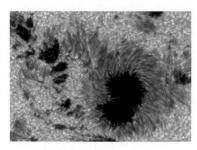

Optical image showing convective granulation cells and several sunspots. Each granule is about 1000 km (621 miles) across and produces a complex network of magnetic fields, which can become concentrated into sunspots.

magnetic fields together into smaller volumes of space, the fields can 'reconnect' into a larger-scale magnetic structure. Enormous energy is released by this process, causing solar flares in which the plasma is temporarily heated to millions of degrees. These become powerful, transient, X-ray sources, and can herald the release of enormous quantities of plasma into interplanetary space, called *coronal mass ejections.*

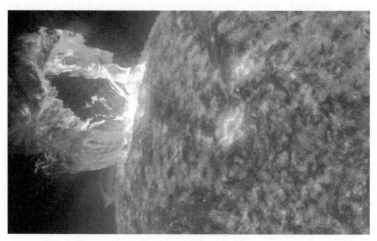

A dramatic solar prominence seen by the NASA SDO spacecraft on 16 April 2012. Plasma from the solar surface is propelled outwards by magnetic lines of force that loop above large sunspot groups.

THE SOLAR CORONA AND SOLAR WIND

Above the photosphere, and extending millions of kilometres into interplanetary space, is a rarefied plasma with temperatures of several million K. The reason for its high temperatures compared to the solar surface of only 5,770 K is still an open issue for research. Current theories suggest that disturbances called *magneto-sonic Alfven waves* that travel along magnetic fields in the plasma may transport enough energy from surface activity into the corona to heat it.

Alongside the corona is an outward flow of plasma called the solar wind, first proposed in the 1950s by Eugene Parker. This wind reaches supersonic speeds within a few million kilometres above the photosphere and travels at a speed ranging from 200 km/sec to over 3,000 km/sec, expanding in a spiral pattern out beyond the orbit of Pluto where it encounters the tenuous gas and dust of the interstellar medium some 120 AU (17.7 billion km or 11 billion miles) from the Sun.

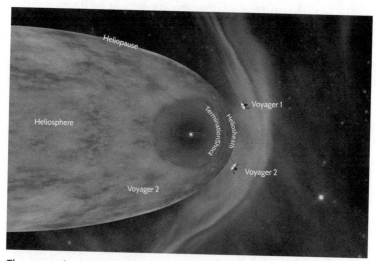

The outer solar wind encounters the heliopause in the direction of the Sun's motion through the Milky Way. This figure shows the main regions of this interface between the interstellar medium (right) and the comet-shaped solar heliosphere.

Key Points

- Our sun is a star, which we can study up close and relate to the billions of other stars we see in the sky.

- Its light and heat are powered by thermonuclear reactions in its core, which fuse hydrogen into helium and release nuclear energy to heat and stabilize the sun against further gravitational collapse.

- The interior of the sun consists of well-defined layers, each with its own unique physical processes.

- The solar surface that we see through a telescope is threaded by magnetic fields, which form many different kinds of structures from sunspots to prominences.

- The corona located above the solar surface is heated by the magnetic activity on the surface and is heated to millions of degrees, which spawns a solar wind that travels throughout interplanetary space.

Chapter 5

Solar Evolution

Like many other stars, the Sun formed from a dense rotating interstellar cloud of gas and dust called a *solar nebula* through the process of gravitational collapse. As it rotated, the cloud became more compact and dense while conserving *angular momentum* (rotational movement about an axis, which remains constant unless acted on by an external force). Within a few million years it had evolved into a flattened disk of circulating matter. At the centre of this disk, most of the mass was concentrated into a dense object several million kilometres in radius, called a *protostar*, but this mass was not stable and continued a slow gravitational collapse to higher densities.

Just as an object dropped from a great height will strike the ground with high kinetic energy, the gas in the collapsing cloud also increased its internal kinetic energy as it 'fell' to smaller sizes. This kinetic energy was randomized and became thermal heat energy, which caused a pressure in the gas opposite to the force of gravity. This caused the collapse to slow down somewhat but nevertheless the core of the cloud kept collapsing, growing in density, and eventually reaching several million Kelvins in temperature. At this point, thermonuclear fusion was triggered at first through the fusion of *deuterium* (an isotope of hydrogen, containing one proton and one neutron) and then at higher temperatures with hydrogen in the P–P cycle. This caused a dramatic rise in plasma temperature and thermal pressure that eventually grew strong enough to balance gravity and cause collapse to slow down and stop. The object ceased to be a protostar and became a stable star. The oldest meteoritic materials in our solar system date from about 4.56 billion years ago, and this is commonly understood to be the current age of our Sun.

The sun as a T-Tauri star with magnetic activity. The circumstellar disk of dust and gas includes magnetic fields, which also flow on to the forming star and release enormous energy, causing flares and a powerful solar wind.

Although after 5 to 10 million years the Sun had stabilized, its surface was still adjusting to the new source of energy at the core, and tremendous convective motions still roiled the surface of the star. Also magnetic fields, trapped in the interstellar matter, flowed from the surrounding disk of matter on to the Sun's surface and produced complex and energetic flares and other activity. A very dense solar wind also emanated from the Sun in this '*T-Tauri*' *phase* (a stage in a young star's development, when temperatures are too low for nuclear fusion). This has consequences for planets forming nearby. This wind is capable of eroding and ejecting interplanetary matter and the atmospheres of nearby planets out to the orbit of Mars. Astronomers have detected many young stars that produce variable light output as well as bursts of X-ray energy, which are also the hallmarks of stars in this very early stage of evolution.

THE MAIN SEQUENCE

As the P–P cycle converts hydrogen into helium, the heavier helium 'ash' diffuses under gravity into the centre of the core. As the P–P reactions continue to deplete hydrogen, they would ordinarily produce less energy. However, this produces a declining pressure causing the core to gravitationally collapse. This collapse increases the temperature of the core and so the reactions actually end up burning more energetically, causing the pressure to increase. These reactions are very sensitive to temperature. For every doubling of the temperature the energy release increases by a factor of almost ten. This makes their energy output about 1 per cent higher every 100 million years, so the Sun gradually becomes more luminous over time, even though the supply of hydrogen is steadily decreasing. By about 5 billion years from now our Sun will be about 70 per cent brighter than it is today.

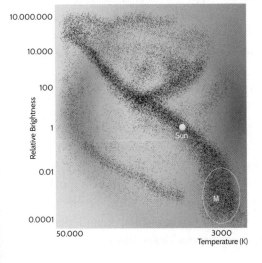

Stars can be organized in the Hertzsprung-Russell (HZ) diagram according to their temperature on the horizontal axis and luminosity on the vertical axis. As a star evolves, it passes through many of the regions in the diagram.

RED GIANT TURNOFF

Eventually, by the time the P–P cycle has converted about 10 per cent of the core hydrogen mass to helium, the core will have collapsed to the point that the hydrogen-rich region just beyond the hydrogen core has reached the P–P-triggering temperature. Over time, there is more energy being produced in this shell zone than in the core. This shell-burning stage causes the Sun to grow in size because more reactions now take place, but also the helium ash core is steadily growing in mass and contracting under gravity, which relentlessly increases the core temperature to over 100 million K.

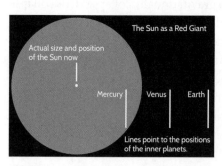

The Sun as a red giant star. The locations of the orbits of the inner planets are shown to indicate the scale of the star.

RED GIANT PHASE

By 7 billion years from now, the shell-burning phase will have dramatically increased the luminosity of our Sun to about 2.2 times its current brightness and over 2,000 times as bright at the peak of this phase. The steady increase in solar luminosity will cause Earth's oceans to evaporate into the atmosphere in another 1 billion years or so, making Earth uninhabitable by organic life as surface temperatures exceeding 100°C (212°F) are achieved and surpassed.

The pace of shell-burning and the depositing of helium ash in the core will make this helium-rich core dense enough that even at temperatures above 100 million K, the matter will start to become degenerate. Instead of thermal pressure supporting it against further collapse, the quantum nature of electrons produces a pressure that resists further collapse and density increase. The mass in this core starts out at about 13 per cent the mass of the Sun or roughly equal to 130 times the mass of Jupiter, but its size will be only slightly bigger than Earth. As shell-burning accelerates over the next 500 million years, the Sun will swell in diameter until it occupies most of the inner solar system out to the orbit of Earth. This expanding outer atmosphere steadily cools to under 4,000 K and the Sun becomes a red giant star, leaving behind in its core a dense, degenerate, earth-sized object called a white dwarf with a mass of about 40 per cent of the Sun.

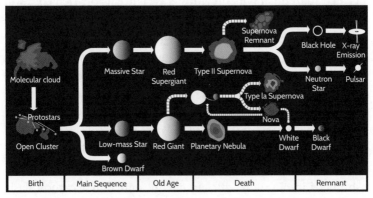

A diagram of the evolution of stars with various masses. The path is complex because the sources of nuclear energy change as a star evolves, and its mass determines the kinds of final states it will achieve.

As this helium core continues to collapse, the temperatures rise above a nuclear threshold where three helium nuclei can fuse to form a carbon nucleus. This transition is so fast that it is called a 'helium flash' event. Within a few minutes, the helium in the core is converted to carbon, releasing an enormous amount of energy almost literally in the blink of an eye. But because the matter in the core is degenerate, it does not act like a normal gas that would increases its pressure as the temperature increases. Instead, nearly all this new energy goes into heating the core so that there is no longer any degeneracy pressure. The core detonates, but as viewed from outside the red giant surface, there is hardly a trace of this event even though its energy release rivals that of all the stars in the Milky Way during this time. The expansion of the core causes the core gases to cool, and this causes the shell-burning hydrogen zone to contract. No longer able to support the balance between gravity and the internal pressure of the extended atmosphere, the star contracts to about 10 times the Sun's current diameter and 40 times its luminosity. Its surface temperature will be near 4000 K, making it an orange–yellow star.

The final 150 million years of the Sun's life will be more complicated than during its previous eras. The carbon-rich core will be surrounded by a helium-rich shell that is busily fusing helium into carbon ash. Outside this shell will be the hydrogen-rich shell where the P–P cycle is providing more than 90 per cent of the Sun's energy. Eventually, as the helium shell depletes itself, the luminosity of the Sun will rise from 40 times to about 100 times its current luminosity as the core slowly collapses and releases gravitational energy, causing the reactions to burn faster. Again the Sun will start to become a red giant, this time with 3,000 times its current luminosity, but now there is no way to fuse carbon ash nuclei into a more efficient energy source in a 'carbon flash' event. Instead, an energy production instability starts that causes the red giant surface to expand and contract every 100,000 years. The Sun shakes itself to death as the outer layers beyond the orbit of Jupiter expand into interstellar space to become a *planetary nebula*. Meanwhile the core has swelled in size and become completely degenerate with a size about that of Earth. When the outer layers of the Sun beyond this core finally dissipate, we are left with

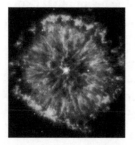

a white dwarf and a planetary nebula as the only signs of a once-stable star.

The Planetary nebula NGC 6751 is recently forming. The diameter is 600 times our solar system. Our Sun will eventually become such a nebula surrounding its white dwarf core located at the centre.

Key Points

- The sun formed from a collapsing cloud of inter-stellar gas about 4.6 billion years ago.

- As a young star forms, its core region heats up until thermonuclear fusion of hydrogen can take place.

- A star spends the majority of its time on the Main Sequence fusing hydrogen fuel into helium until 20 per cent of the hydrogen is consumed.

- A star leaves the Main Sequence and evolves into a red giant star in which complex changes occur in its core causing, the star to expand and cool.

- Eventually the fusion mechanism of available fuels such as hydrogen, helium and carbon are exhausted and a star like our sun evolves into a white dwarf surrounded by a planetary nebula.

Chapter 6

Space Weather

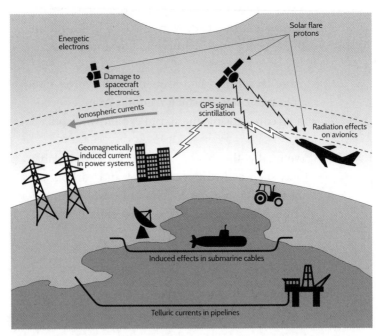

The various impacts of space weather illustrating the complexity of the many technological systems that are affected by solar particles and radiation during space weather 'solar storm' events.

The Sun emits a very strong wind from its outer layers, and this wind flows past Mercury, Venus and the rest of the planets in the solar system. In fact, you can even say that Earth goes around the Sun while still being inside the atmosphere of the Sun. Even if you were in space you wouldn't notice anything happening at all. This wind is billions of times more dilute than any wind we feel on the ground, but is easily detected by satellite sensors.

The surface of the Sun is a magnetically complicated plasma that can sometimes be ejected by the sun in events called 'solar flares' and 'coronal mass ejections'.

Solar flares are quite spectacular and deadly. Within an hour or less, an area of the Sun the size of Earth suddenly ejects a burst of X-rays and other powerful radiations. Travelling at the speed of light, it still takes 8½ minutes for these X-rays to reach the Earth. During some of the most powerful solar flares, an astronaut in a spacesuit could be killed if carrying out a spacewalk at the time. NASA, and astronomers, have been studying solar flares for over 50 years to learn more about what causes them, and to make it easier to forecast when the next one will happen so that astronauts will be safe.

Fortunately, the atmosphere of Earth is so thick that we never have to worry about even the most powerful solar flares here on the ground. The only thing that solar flares do is to knockout short-wave radio communication during the daytime. These blasts of X-rays damage a part of the atmosphere called the *ionosphere*, which lets radio signals from the ground get reflected like light is reflected from a mirror. The X-rays from a solar flare

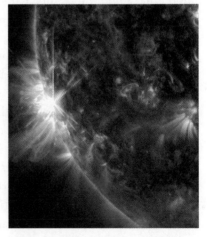

A solar flare detected at X-ray energies by the Solar Dynamics Observatory. The event was so intense that it caused the X-shaped linear pattern centred on the brightest region near the limb of the Sun.

A major coronal mass ejection observed in 2017. This composite image produced by the SOHO satellite shows both the solar photosphere and the coronal streamers and outflows from the ejection event.

can cause changes that absorb the radio energy from a reflected short-wave signal and cause a fade-out in reception.

The second type of storm from the Sun is the coronal mass ejection (CME). For reasons that solar physicists still don't fully understand, the Sun occasionally ejects huge clouds of plasma into space. These clouds can be sent out in any direction, but with a frequency of every few weeks during the sunspot maximum period there is a strong likelihood that some will be directed at Earth. CMEs travel at about two million kilometres an hour and take two to three days to get here. By the time they reach the orbit of Earth, these plasma clouds have grown to be millions of kilometres across.

It just so happens that Earth has a strong magnetic field, and a very thick atmosphere, so we never have to worry about CME clouds as they sweep by Earth on their way to Pluto and beyond. Earth's magnetic field pushes most of the particles in these clouds away from us so they never really hit the planet at all. But even so, the CME material can make lots of trouble in other ways too.

As the material streams past Earth, it stretches Earth's magnetic field. This makes Earth's magnetic field look like a comet with Earth at the head of it. The tail of Earth's field trembles and shakes, and sometimes it can even snap. When that happens, space weather becomes more than just some invisible storm between the planets.

In a region of the tail nearly halfway to the Moon, there are charged particles trapped in the magnetic field – mostly electrons and protons. When the field changes shape in what physicists call

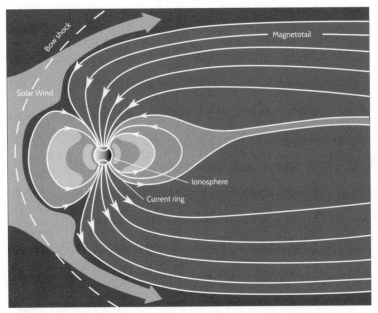

Earth's magnetic field distorted by space weather. The solar wind enters from the left and applies pressure to the magnetic field as it passes over it, deforming it into a comet-like shape.

a magnetic reconnection event, these particles pick up energy from the magnetic field, and begin to move at very high speeds. Within a few minutes, they travel towards Earth along the magnetic field. They get funnelled into the polar regions, where they collide with atoms of oxygen and nitrogen. These collisions give off light, and we see this from the ground as the famous *aurora borealis* and *aurora australis* – the northern and southern lights. People have worried about them for centuries, but they really are harmless. They can't get any closer to the ground than 100 km (70 miles) or so, but optical illusions can fool the eye into thinking they get much lower and even touch the ground.

A solar flare erupting on the sun will create a sudden ionospheric disturbance (SID) 8½ minutes later, which causes shortwave blackouts and a very sharp change in Earth's magnetism detected at ground level. The white light flare seen by Richard

Carrington and Richard Hodgson on 1 September 1859 was followed immediately by SID disturbances seen at several magnetic observatories in England and India.

Powerful flares almost always lead to the launch of a CME from the same magnetically active region on the Sun. When this CME arrives at Earth it produces powerful and sudden changes in Earth's magnetic field. We know from this that the 1859 CME travelled 150 million km (93 million miles) in 17.6 hours, for a breathtaking speed of 2,370 km/s (5.3 million mph). The CME on 4 August 1972 made it from the sun to Earth in 14.6 hours for a speed of 2,850 km/s (6.4 million mph), which is nearly one per cent the speed of light!

Don Neidig, a solar physicist at the National Solar Observatory, calculated that the 1859 Carrington-Hodgson flare produced 2×10^{30} ergs of energy in a matter of five minutes. Only one other flare, one on 24 April 1984 with an estimated yield of 6×10^{30} ergs, produced as much or more energy.

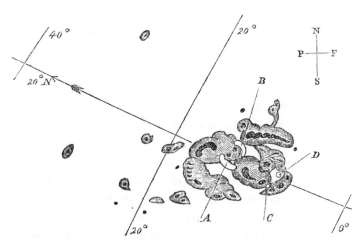

Richard Carrington's diagram of the 1859 solar flare. The brilliant features marked A, B, C and D lasted only 5–10 minutes before fading away. No similar event has been observed in the 150 years since.

When the CMEs from solar storms arrive, they compress Earth's magnetic field and set in motion a number of processes. Oxygen ions are pumped out of Earth's polar regions and trapped into a 'ring current' over the equator. This current of particles strengthens within a few hours and creates its own magnetic field. Earth's field is reduced in strength. Meanwhile, as auroras turn on over the poles and expand toward the equator, they bring with them their own currents of particles flowing in the ionosphere. Usually, a severe storm reduces Earth's equatorial magnetism by just under 0.5 per cent. During a September 1989 storm, the effect was 3 per cent. By comparison, in March 1989 a storm that blacked out Quebec caused a 1 per cent decrease in Earth's magnetism.

TECHNOLOGY IMPACTS

If auroras were the only things that space weather causes, we wouldn't have much to really worry about, but unfortunately it is not that simple. We rely on communications satellites, military satellites, and a reliable electrical service to power our computers, televisions and air conditioners and to run our industries. Space weather can knock out satellites and even cause blackouts!

In March 1989, the Canadian province of Quebec experienced a blackout that affected millions of people for a half a day. People were stuck in dark elevators, heating systems would not work to heat homes during the Canadian winter, and if it hadn't been for a bit of old-fashioned good luck, many states from Maine to Georgia would have had electrical problems as well. It was triggered by a huge solar storm that caused currents of electricity to flow in the ground under Canada. These currents found their way into the Quebec electrical power system. In 90 seconds, the engineers went from normal operation to full blackout.

Severe solar storms have wreaked havoc with virtually every aspect of communications technology. There were even electrical blackouts and satellite outages thrown in for good measure. The human costs of this solar violence are measured in billions of dollars of lost satellites, and millions of hours of lost productivity as humans sat idle waiting for the storms to pass. There are even grave national security issues raised by communications and electrical power blackouts occurring by accident at strategically critical times.

Solar flares, and the hailstorms of high-energy electrons and protons that come out of them, are a potent problem. These particles collide with the atoms that make up the walls of the satellite and produce secondary showers of particles that flow deep into the satellite's interior where they interact with integrated circuits and other components carrying millions of sub-microscopic wires and connections between resistors and transistors and the microchips. One well-placed 'zap' by one of these shower particles can cause electrical currents to flow to make a logic element think that it is a '1' not a '0'. These kinds of phantom bit-switching events can lead to a garbled command and corrupted data, causing the satellite to malfunction or to fail. At the present time, there are some 800 working satellites in orbit performing a variety of important functions. They collectively cost just under $100 billion to build, and another $40 billion to launch.

Key Points

- Space weather is a system of matter and energy flows from the solar surface that can cause technological disturbances here on Earth, and is generally correlated with the sunspot cycle.

- Space weather consists of the solar wind and its changes, as well as transient phenomena such as solar flares and coronal mass ejections.

- Particles from coronal mass ejections can travel to earth and cause disturbances that give rise to the aurora borealis and aurora australis.

- Energetic particles can also invade spacecraft and satellite electronics and cause damage to delicate circuitry.

- Geomagnetic storms caused by coronal mass ejection plasma can produce sub-surface currents that can invade our electric power grid and cause transformer damage and blackouts.

PART III
Planetary Systems

Chapter 7

The Solar System

For millennia, the solar system was known to contain eight major objects: the Sun, Moon, Mercury, Venus, Mars, Jupiter and Saturn and of course our Earth. Little was known about them and it was speculated that they were balls of luminous gas orbiting Earth while affixed to rotating nested spherical shells of a crystalline or other material. It wasn't until the detailed observations by Tycho Brahe in the late 1500s and the detailed studies of Tycho's data by Johannes Kepler that these ancient ideas were finally abandoned. The movement of the Great Comet of 1577 showed a path that intersected the crystalline spheres, destroying them, while Tycho's Nova of 1572 had previously showed no change of sky position as viewed by Tycho and observers in Europe, so it must be well beyond the orbit of the moon and a part of the presumably changeless celestial sphere.

The work by Kepler to test Tycho's high-precision planetary data against the prevailing models for planetary orbits led to three remarkable conclusions, which are known as Kepler's Laws of Planetary Motion. First, the planets orbited the sun on elliptical, not circular paths. Second, the speeds of the planets are such that they sweep out equal areas in equal times. Finally, Kepler's Third Law states that the orbital distance from the sun (a) and the period of the orbit (T) are equal to each other according to $T^2 = a^3$ when the planet distances are in units of the Earth-Sun distance, and the orbit period is given in Earth years. For example, Jupiter's period is T = 11.9 Earth years so if $T^2 = a^3$, then a = 5.2 AUs. Sir Isaac Newton later explained these laws by using his theory of universal gravitation, and went on to show how Kepler's Third Law could be used to measure the mass of a planet once the orbit of its satellite was known. This would turn out to be a powerful method that could even be extended to measuring the masses of stars and whole galaxies.

The basic landscape of our solar system has been known for over a century, but has steadily been improved in detail and inventory thanks to robotic spacecraft observations and Earth-based investigations with optical, radio and infrared telescopes largely begun in the early 1960s. This chapter only touches upon the highlights and implications of this knowledge.

LARGE BODIES

There are eight major planets in the solar system, including four rocky 'terrestrial' planets (Mercury, Venus, Earth and Mars), two gas giants (Jupiter and Saturn) and two ice giants (Uranus and Neptune). There are also six identified dwarf planets: Pluto, Makemake, Ceres, Charon, Eris and Haumea, although this list will continue to grow as more large objects are detected in the outermost regions of the solar system beyond the orbit of Neptune. The distinction between a planet and a dwarf planet was established by the International Astronomical Union in 2005, with the result that Pluto – previously regarded as the ninth planet – was demoted to dwarf planet status. There is now a generation of children born after 2005 who will never know Pluto as the ninth planet but who may eventually hear about a true ninth planet as astronomers search for a massive Earth-sized world orbiting far beyond Pluto in a region called the Kuiper Belt (see opposite).

By 2019, all the major bodies in the solar system had been visited by spacecraft that made on-the-spot imaging studies of their accessible surfaces and measurements of local particle and magnetic field conditions. Several bodies, such as Venus, the

Moon, Mars and Titan (the largest moon of Saturn), have been the direct subjects of surface studies by landers or rovers. The four giant outer planets do not have physical surfaces or conditions that would allow landings, but the atmospheres of Jupiter and Saturn have been examined by spacecraft plunging into them and beaming back data before the enormous planetary pressures destroy them. The properties of the planets accessible from external observations can be fully understood through remote imaging and on-the-spot spacecraft observations. But the details of their internal structures remain mostly speculation until they can be studied using seismic stations for the inner, rocky worlds, or with robotic probes for the gas and ice giants.

SMALLER BODIES AND SOLAR SYSTEM RUBBLE

There are two belts of material left over from our solar system's planet-building era. The first is the asteroid belt between the orbits of Mars and Jupiter, which has over 100,000 identified asteroids ranging in size from minute dust grains – viewed from Earth as the Zodiacal Light – to the dwarf planet Ceres at over 950 km (590 miles) in diameter. The total mass of the asteroid belt is about 4 per cent that of our Moon. The second belt of material is the Kuiper Belt, which includes objects with orbits beginning near the region of Neptune and likely extending over 150 billion km (93 billion miles) from the Sun. About 1,000 bodies larger than

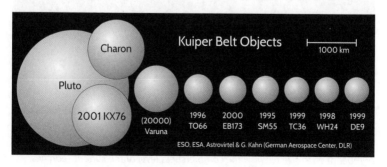

The largest objects in the Kuiper Belt discovered by 2018.

a few kilometres have been discovered in the Kuiper Belt so far. The Kuiper Belt extends into an area called the Oort Cloud, which is believed to be a large reservoir of comet nuclei ejected from the inner solar system by Jupiter. It extends about 0.5 light years from the Sun in a roughly spherical cloud, hence the name.

The Minor Planets Center is the central reporting agency that holds the official sightings and orbital records for all objects in the solar system from metre-sized asteroids to the satellites of each planet. Currently, over 650,000 small bodies are known, and thousands of new ones are discovered every year. Of particular concern are the 18,000 near Earth objects (NEOs) whose orbits come within 30 million km (18 million miles) of Earth. Among the NEO population are the potentially hazardous objects (PHOs) numbering 1,400 identified objects whose current orbits are within 20 lunar distances (6 million km = 4 million miles) of

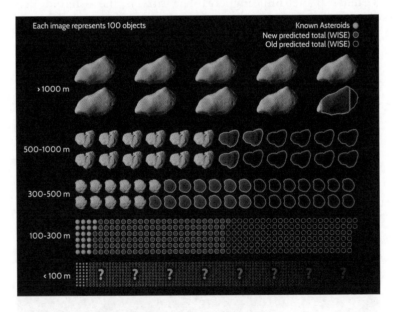

A comparison of the detected asteroids at different sizes with the predicted number at each size to show the completeness level of the current searches, and what is left to discover.

Earth. Based on the current orbital data and computation limits, PHOs may pose a high risk of collision with Earth. The vast majority of these objects, so far, are less than a few hundred metres across, but it is believed they represent only 20 per cent of a much larger population of small bodies yet to be discovered. Based on discovery rates, it is believed that 93 per cent of all PHOs larger

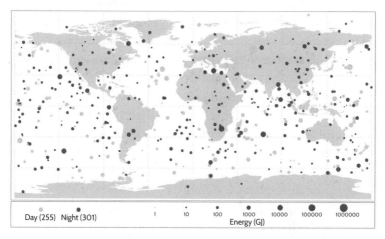

Day (255) Night (301)   1   10   100   1000   10000   100000   1000000
Energy (GJ)

The most brilliant meteors are called bolides. This map shows sightings of bolides since 1988. The largest of these are objects are 20 m (65 ft) across, with impact energies up to 10,000 tons of TNT.

than 1 km (⅝ mile) have been identified. Since 2015, more than 1500 previously unknown NEOs have been discovered each year. The estimated population of NEOs larger than 140 metres (459 feet) is about 25,000, so only six per cent of these potentially devastating asteroids have as yet been discovered.

About 50,000 tons of material strikes Earth every year, but the majority of this mass is dust and small objects below one metre across. The frequency of terrestrial impacts is such that every 30 seconds an object about 1 mm (⅜ in) in diameter enters Earth's atmosphere, while metre-sized objects arrive once a year. On the larger scale, 100 m (328 ft) objects capable of creating craters like the Barringer Crater in Arizona are once in 50,000-year events, while 10 km (6¼ mile) extinction-level events occur about once every 100 million years. The most dramatic recent impact was the February 2013 Chelyabinsk Event by a 20 m (65½ ft), once-a-century, body. This caused over 3,000 injuries and considerable damage to this small Russian town. The air-burst energy of this blast was equal to 500,000 tonnes of TNT or a small atomic bomb.

Although photographic detection remains one of the most effective ways for identifying and cataloguing interplanetary bodies, other approaches also provide insight into how vulnerable we are.

As objects enter the atmosphere, they produce intense pulses of infrasound energy at frequencies too low for humans to detect. Sensitive infrasound detectors across the globe have been installed by military observers to detect violations of the Nuclear Test Ban Treaty. In an instant, small nuclear devices exploded above ground can be detected anywhere on the surface of Earth, but over the years there have been an increasing list of false alarms due to large asteroids entering the atmosphere. For example, on October 7, 2008, a small 80 tonne asteroid named 2008 TC3 was detected in space about 19 hours prior to its impact on the Earth. It detonated 37 km (23 miles) above the ground with an energy equivalent to 2000 tonnes of TNT. Infrasound data have been used to estimate that 30 objects with detonation yields of more than 100 tonnes of TNT explode in the atmosphere every year. So in addition to the larger 100 m (328 ft) class objects that can be detected while still in space, there is a significant population of still smaller objects that cannot be detected before they make impact with Earth. Objects of this size tend to explode in the atmosphere and pose a substantially reduced human hazard.

Landscape on Mars viewed by NASA's Curiosity rover from its vantage point within Gale Crater in 2019, showing 1 cm (⅜ in) stones in the foreground and distant hills and mountains.

SURFACE EXPLORATION

The list of objects in the solar system for which we now have kilometre-scale images or better is an impressive one. Including Mercury, Venus, Mars and our Moon, the total surface area of the 22 moons, six asteroids and six comets amounts to 285 million square km (110 million square miles) or about twice the land area of Earth. Our Moon's entire surface has been mapped to 2 m (6½ ft) resolution by NASA's Lunar Reconnaissance Orbiter satellite, and several robotic rovers are in operation on the surface of Mars, with landings on Venus and Titan having been accomplished in the late 20th century.

Surface exploration remains one of the most challenging and costly means for direct studies of the geology and minerology of planetary, asteroidal and cometary surfaces. However, progress in this research continues to advance every decade. Rovers equipped with sophisticated telerobotics and instrumentation can perform on-the-spot chemical assays of minerals, as demonstrated by the Mars Curiosity Rover. Lunar rovers have now been fielded by US, Russian, Chinese and Indian space agencies. Surface comet and asteroid samplers and rovers (hoppers!) are now steadily increasing in numbers, and in the 2020s the first rover mission to Europa will be launched, with eventual plans to return to Mercury and Venus. The principle driver for rover technology is to assess surface minerology for use by future astronauts as rocket fuel, water, and building materials, but also in the search for the conditions required for life. In the case of Europa and Mars, these locations are receiving the highest level of scrutiny and investment.

THE SEARCH FOR LIFE

For decades it was thought that liquid water, an essential ingredient for life, was only found on Earth. Since the 1980s, and with the help of the Voyager, Galileo and Cassini spacecraft, evidence for liquid water has been discovered below the surface of the Jovian moons Europa and Ganymede, and apparently beneath the icy crust of Saturn's moon Enceladus, whose water geysers were discovered by Cassini in 2006.

Among the rocky terrestrial planets, water ice has been detected in the permanently shadowed craters on the poles of Mercury and the Moon. On Mars, many different geological signs suggest running water has existed in the recent past, and in some cases is present today, as well as the discovery of a vast subsurface lake of liquid water detected in 2018 beneath the south polar cap. Traces of organic molecules have also been detected on the red planet, including an annual increase and decrease in atmospheric methane.

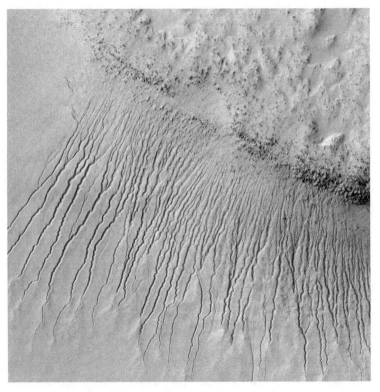

The Mars Reconnaissance Orbiter images a portion of the Hellas impact basin, revealing numerous rivulets that lead from a subsurface aquifer (top) down slope (bottom). These channels may be only a few years old since they have not as yet been covered by dust storm activity.

The possibility that life may exist on other bodies in the solar system has been given a boost by studies of extremophile bacteria on Earth, which have revealed that life is far more robust than previously thought. Signs of bacterial life have been found many miles below the surface of Earth. Extremophile bacteria have been found living under the near-boiling conditions of hot springs, geysers and submarine hydrothermal vents. Anaerobic bacteria not only survive well without oxygen to provide energy, but have been found respiring a whole host of other chemicals such as hydrogen sulphide and formate. Some species called endoliths are perfectly happy living inside solid rock. These enormous possibilities for redefining life have spurred attempts by NASA to actively explore the solar system bodies with the presumption that life may abound under many conditions previously thought to be hostile to life. Even radiation is no longer considered a severe problem for organism survival. In 1969, Apollo 12 astronauts returned samples from the Surveyor 3 spacecraft, which landed in 1967, and found surviving *Streptococcus mitis* bacteria. This finding dramatically increased NASA's protocols for spacecraft decontamination prior to launch so that terrestrial life doesn't accidentally hitchhike to other solar system locations and contaminate the life-signs found there. Most of the search for signs of life on Mars now involve subsurface studies where the biota would be shielded from surface radiation and ultraviolet light, and have access to known sub-surface aquifers.

Key Points

- The solar system contains eight major planets and millions of smaller bodies called asteroids and comets, which all orbit our sun.

- Earth is literally situated within an interplanetary 'shooting gallery' and is bombarded by thousands of meteorites every year from dust grain 'shooting stars' to objects tens of meters across. The larger of these, though infrequent, can cause severe property damage and even death.

- The exploration and mapping of all planetary and minor-body surfaces is an ongoing process to complete a full assay of the minerology and evolution of our solar system over billions of years.

- The discovery of extremophile bacteria on Earth, and liquid water or solid ice among the planetary and asteroidal surfaces, has ignited a search for signs of life, fossil or living, beyond Earth.

- Surface exploration using robotic rovers such as Curiosity on Mars is the most economical means for exploring planetary surfaces for purposes of determining basic surface chemistry and the conditions for living systems.

Chapter 8

Solar System Formation

Among the earliest and most successful theories to explain the origin of our solar system and of Earth itself was the Nebular Hypothesis, proposed by philosopher Immanuel Kant in 1755. He suggested that the solar system formed from a cloud of gas that collapsed to form a disk and a central massive core from which the Sun formed. The details of this basic plan would be refined over the next few centuries to become the present model of solar system formation.

Stars and planetary systems form from dense collections of matter called *molecular clouds* that are typically several light years across. These normally stable clouds become destabilized and small regions begin to gravitationally collapse while conserving angular momentum. This results in a rotating, flattened disk that accounts for the long-known fact that the orbit planes of the planets all fall within a narrow range close to the solar equatorial plane. For the solar system, the reason for this cloud destabilization may have been the impact of a supernova remnant shock wave. This is indicated by the presence of the aluminum-26 isotope, whose daughter products are found in many meteorites. This isotope has a half-life of only 700,000 years, so it was deposited into the *primordial molecular cloud* very quickly. This implies a very close-by supernova event near the pre-solar system molecular cloud. Meteoritic samples also show the presence of micron-sized granules.

These are silicon-rich interstellar dust grains that were produced in the atmospheres of red supergiant stars and incorporated into the pre-solar system molecular cloud during its initial condensation from the interstellar medium. The oldest meteorites, such as the 4.56 billion year Northwest Africa NWA1119 meteorite found in 2018, date from a time about 10 million years before planet-building took place, and show that igneous processes are taking place, probably during collisions between *planetesimals* (small bodies formed of dust and rock fragments that combine to form larger bodies and ultimately planets).

Artist rendering of the disk orbiting the star Beta Pictoris, which may resemble that of our own solar system 4.5 billion years ago.

The ancient disk matter began as simple gas and dust, with the dust grains being the reservoirs for all elements and compounds that have a solid state at low temperature, including carbon- and silicate-rich rocks, and ices of water, methane and other compounds. Known as *protoplanetary disks*, they have been detected directly in a variety of locations throughout nearby regions of the Milky Way. One such environment is the Orion Molecular Cloud, in which the Hubble Space Telescope has been able to image hundreds of these disks since 1993. Having formed so close to massive stars with intense ultraviolet radiation fields, these disks are slowly being evaporated away, perhaps before they can produce planets or even a central star. In other locations, these disks can be detected by their infrared dust emissions or even at sub-millimetre wavelengths (ALMA array). These disks can vary in size from 15 AU to over 200 AU depending on the mass of the central star. Often they are observed edge-on as dark disks that split an optical nebula into two parts. This occurs because as the protostar evolves, disk gases can be ionized to form nebulae that emit light above and below the disk plane.

Astronomers have long studied the infrared properties of these disks at various ages, including those around older stars in which the interplanetary gas has been ejected, leaving only the dust grains, asteroids and comets behind as 'rubble disks'. They are seen orbiting the stars Vega and Fomalhaut. Detailed theoretical modelling indicates that dust grains as small as a few microns are abundant, though often absent from the interiors of these disks where radiation pressure ejects them to form an evacuated central hole in the disk.

These small grains collide and fuse, growing into meteorite-sized bodies centimetres across, which in turn grow into 10-km (6¼ mile) planetesimals over the course of several million years depending on the gas and dust density of the local material. The collisions the planetesimals at high speed often shatter them, but low-speed collisions cause them to merge and grow into planet-sized cores of several thousand kilometres. A fossil of this process has been seen by the New Horizons spacecraft in its 2019 fly-by of a distant solar system object named Ultima Thule that orbits the sun in the Kuiper Belt. Depending on the availability of additional matter, these planetary cores cease to grow further to become small-sized planets, or grow by gravitational accretion into massive ice or gas giants.

The composition of the interplanetary material depends on its distance from the Sun. A combination of chemical reactions, density and heating ensures that close to the Sun, the dominant

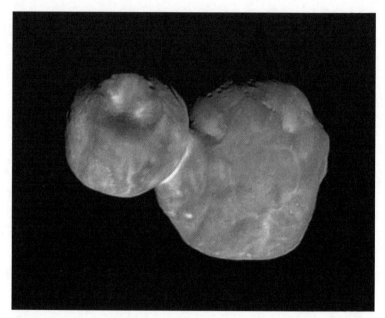

Ultima Thule is an object formed by the collision of two smaller bodies. When collisions are gentle, objects can merge together to form more massive bodies.

compounds are rich in iron and silicate compounds because these have a very high melting and vaporization temperature. At about the orbit of Mars, at a point called the *Frost Line*, temperatures in the disk have cooled to the point where ices may form, and so dust grains develop thick mantles of condensed ices. The small planets and moons in the solar system today very accurately reflect this kind of chemical segregation, with asteroids and small bodies being rocky materials, and moons and bodies beyond the Frost Line being essentially balls of ice.

Astronomers have investigated a variety of objects over the decades and found examples of nearly every stage in solar system formation. Molecular clouds discovered in the mid-1970s are ubiquitous in the Milky Way. Several stellar nurseries have been identified close by the Sun, including the Orion Molecular Cloud with its famous Orion Nebula, as well as smaller clouds such as the Taurus Molecular Cloud only 400 light years from the Sun, which has infrared sources identified as newly formed stars still embedded in the dusty, molecular material.

Calculations and computer models show that planet formation lasts tens of millions of years. For the largest planets, this has a direct and visible impact upon the shape of the disk. Although the smaller bodies grow by collisions due to their geometric areas, once a planet grows to more than about 50 times the mass of Earth, its gravitational influences start to greatly exceed the planet's geometric area. Acting like gravitational vacuum cleaners, the giant planets sweep out circumstellar zones in the shape of rings that are millions of miles across, which can be seen from Earth using telescopes such as the Atacama Large Millimeter Array (ALMA). The image of the disk surrounding the young star HL Tauri shows this effect.

Although it may take a small planet tens of millions of years to grow to its final size, a giant planet can reach Jovian masses in only a few million years. Towards the end, huge quantities of primordial disk gases are accreted into massive gaseous envelopes surrounding the growing planets. For Jupiter and Saturn, these became the gas giants of the solar system. For Uranus and Neptune, they never quite reached this accretion phase and so are massive balls of ice with much smaller atmospheres. One thing that has become known from studying the element abundances of the outer planets is that they could not have formed where we see them today.

Studies of planets orbiting other stars, which astronomers call exoplanets, reveal that so-called 'Hot Jupiters' (Jupiter-sized planets orbiting very close to their stars) are common, which has dramatic consequences for planet-building. For some stars, the disks are massive enough that their gravity can cause newly formed giant planets to migrate inwards towards their central stars over timescales as short as a few million years. Along the way, they are capable of gravitationally ejecting all of the newly formed smaller planets. In our solar system, the disk was not massive enough for Jupiter and Saturn to migrate inside the orbit of Mercury, and the process ceased when they reached their present distances. This allowed the inner terrestrial planets to continue to form and establish their orbits. An important additional feature is that Jupiter and Saturn served as strong perturbers of the orbits of asteroids and comets, ejecting them out of the inner solar system and deep into the Oort Cloud. This had the salutary effect of shielding the surfaces of the inner planets from continual comet and asteroid bombardment in the ensuing billions of years of history, which probably allowed life to flourish on Earth.

LATE HEAVY BOMBARDMENT

Evidence to show how catastrophic this planet-building period was is written on the cratered surfaces of every solid body in the solar system, even on small asteroids no more than a few kilometres across.

During this formative period of planet-building, there was a very large population of planetesimals of 500–1,000 km (311–620 miles) size in complex orbits throughout the inner solar system. Some of these may have been ejected through the gravitational action of Jupiter, but in several cases, they were among the last objects to collide with the surfaces of the inner planets. The surface of the Moon and Mars show very large impact basins formed by planetesimal impact during the Late Heavy Bombardment era (4.1 to 3.8 billion years ago). Mare Orientale (Moon) and Hellas Panitia and Utopia (Mars) are thought to have formed in this way. Even in the outer solar system, Saturn's moon Mimas, only 400 km (248 miles) in diameter, has a crater – Herschel – that is 130 km (81 miles) across. Based on its composition, Mimas would have shattered by this impact had the moon been 30 per cent smaller.

The origin of the Moon is now widely accepted by astronomers as a collision event that took place about 100 million years after Earth's initial formation, involving a planetesimal about the size of Mars. This object gouged out enough mass to enable the formation of our own Moon. Supercomputer models of this encounter suggest the formation of a massive Saturn-like disk encircling the Earth's equator, which later cooled and condensed into the Moon. The amount of kinetic energy liberated by this event was enough to reliquify the entire surface of Earth. Nevertheless, within a few hundred million years of the event, Earth's surface cooled so that liquid water, perhaps from water-rich comet collisions, could begin to fill the oceans. The first traces of life (chemical traces rather than fossils) have been claimed to have been found in rocks dating from about 500 million years after the impact.

Artistic rendering of the formation of our Moon from a giant impact. The event liquified the surface of Earth and ejected matter into a circum-Earth ring from which our Moon accumulated.

Key Points

- The initial collapse of the interstellar cloud that formed our Sun and solar system may have involved the detonation of a nearby supernova.

- The initial disk of gas and dust evolved into a vast system of coagulated asteroids and larger-sized bodies, which accreted to form the planets, although some of this rubble is now present in the form of asteroids and cometary bodies.

- Planets formed rapidly within a few millions years, but also migrated from more distant locations, especially the more massive planets such as Jupiter, Saturn, Uranus and Neptune.

- During the last stages of planet formation, the solid crusts of the forming planets underwent a massive bombardment period lasting a billion years. The violence of this period can be seen in the pockmarked surfaces of the asteroids and moons across the solar system.

- Our moon arose from the collision of Earth with a Mars-sized planet, whose material created a ring around Earth out of which the Moon accumulated about 100 million years after Earth formed.

Chapter 9

Exoplanets

The existence of planets beyond our solar system, called exoplanets, was mostly an issue of speculation and science fiction until measurements of the nearby Barnard's Star in the early 1960s by Peter van de Kamp seemed to suggest the presence of a Jupiter-sized planet. Although its existence was subsequently disproven, this led to a redoubling of efforts to detect exoplanets in the decades that followed. The 1970s and 1980s were frustrating times for exoplanet searches because the limits of the technology only allowed the discovery of binary stars in which the smaller companion was a red dwarf star and not a less massive planet. Then, in 1992, a discovery occurred that dramatically inspired exoplanet searches.

Aleksander Wolszczan and Dale Frail discovered two small planets orbiting the pulsar PSR 1257+12 located 2,300 light years from Earth in the constellation Virgo. A pulsar is a rotating neutron star (see page 132) that emits a powerful beam of electromagnetic energy, detected as a regular pulse of radiation (hence the name). Based on the slight changes in the pulsar spin and orbit periods, Wolszczan and Frail calculated that the planets were 0.02, 3.9 and 4.3 times the mass of the Earth, and orbited closer to the pulsar than Venus and Mercury do to our Sun. But before astronomers could fully digest how such planets could form in the vicinity of a neutron star remnant of a supernova, new discoveries began to be made.

In 1995, Michel Mayor and Didier Queloz detected an exoplanet orbiting the star 51 Pegasi, a sun-like star located 50 light years from Earth. The planet (51 Pegasi b) was about half the mass of Jupiter and orbited closer to its star than Mercury does to our Sun, completing one orbit every four days. Its estimated surface temperature exceeded 1,500 K (1,226°C). This was soon followed in 1996 by the discoveries of 47 Ursa Majoris b and, in 1998, Gliese 876 b by Geoffrey Marcy and Paul Butler, using the radial velocity method. In 1999, the exoplanet HD 209458 b was detected by radial velocity and then confirmed by David Charbonneau using the transit method – the first use of this method to detect exoplanets.

Since the 1990s, and the important validation of the transit and radial velocity methods for efficiently detecting exoplanets, a tremendous effort among ground-based observatories led to the discovery of 84 exoplanets by 2010, including several planetary systems with two or more planets. The launch of the NASA Kepler Observatory in 2010 dramatically changed the pace of exoplanet discoveries. Kepler monitored the light from 150,000 Sun-like stars in a small patch of the constellation Cygnus. The 2010 sample included over 700 exoplanet candidates and the detailed properties of over 300 from as small as Earth to much larger than Jupiter. By October 2018, the list of confirmed exoplanets from ground and space-based studies has grown to 3,851 exoplanets in 2,871 planetary systems. Their details can now be found in the Extrasolar Planets Encyclopaedia. This list includes a number of exoplanets that have now been directly imaged using ground-based telescopes. These include three Jupiter-sized planets orbiting the star HR8799 located 129 light years from Earth. What astronomers have learned from this huge ensemble of exoplanets has revolutionized our understanding of what constitutes a 'normal' planetary system, the frequency of planets with various masses, and insights into the formation and evolution of planetary systems.

PLANETARY FREQUENCIES

The Holy Grail of exoplanetary exploration is to find a twin planet to our Earth. This requires that the planet not only has the same or similar mass as our Earth, but that it orbits within a range of distances from its star called the habitable zone (HZ). This zone is a range of distances from an exoplanet's central star where surface temperatures allow water to be in liquid form. In our solar system, this zone extends from about the orbit of Venus to the orbit of Mars. A recalculation of how broad this zone should be by NASA astronomer Edward Schwieterman in 2019 accounts for the effects of the greenhouse gas carbon dioxide and suggests a zone much narrower than for previous liquid-water-only definitions. Nevertheless, the 'HZ' is our best estimate for where planets with living biospheres might exist based on remote telescopic studies.

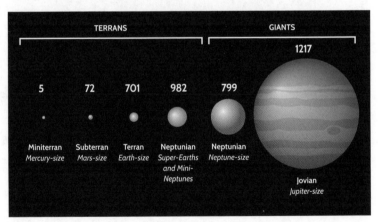

The frequency of the known exoplanets by mass. Although current methods favour detecting planets larger than Uranus, significant numbers of Earth-sized worlds have also been found.

Exoplanets can be summarized by their size and mass frequency. This is a tally of how many exoplanets you find within a large sample as a function of their mass or size. Current techniques favour the detection of the largest exoplanets. Nevertheless, the current sample includes over 773 exoplanets that have masses between that of Mars and Earth. It should be remarked, however, that in our solar system the 'Neptunian and Jovian' planets have satellites nearly as large as the terrestrial planets but these Earth-sized moons cannot be detected with current technology, so the above tally may

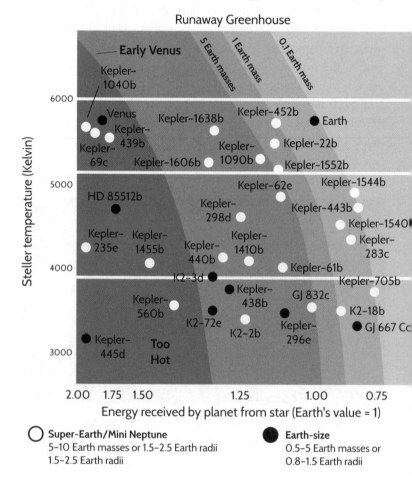

The locations of known Earth-sized exoplanets relative to their star's habitable zone boundaries. The locations of Venus, Earth and Mars are shown for comparison. Within the Runaway Greenhouse band, planetary carbon dioxide and water vapour cause rapid heating of planetary surfaces and even loss of atmosphere.

include many more bodies of terrestrial size in the star's HZ.

The location of an exoplanet is nearly as important as its mass if one is looking for prospective planets where life based on liquid water might be possible.

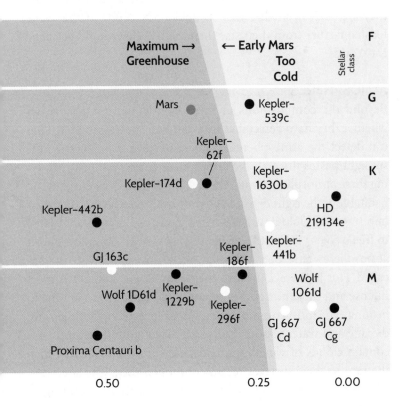

Mars-size
0.1–0.5 Earth masses or
0.4–0.8 Earth radius

An important property of a planet is its mass–radius relationship. This can be used to infer an average density and from this a crude model of its composition: rocky vs gaseous. A number of exoplanets smaller than about three times Earth's radius have now been measured to independently gauge their radii and masses. The work by astronomer Sara Gettel and David Charbonneau in 2016 shows that at about a mass of five times our Earth the exoplanet transitions from a mostly rocky world to one in which water dominates. These 'Water Worlds' in the habitable zone would likely have few continental masses. Because they are slightly smaller than Uranus or Neptune, if they were located farther from their star than the HZ, they would be called Ice Worlds.

ATMOSPHERES

Beyond the compositions of these worlds, the question arises whether they have detectable atmospheres. Spectroscopic studies can detect the atmospheres of many of these exoplanets as the sunlight passes through the atmosphere during a transit. Studying these atmospheres would be the first step to decide if they are habitable at the right density and pressure, and whether they contain traces of biologically produced gases such as ozone (related to free oxygen) and nitrogen. By 2018, over two dozen exoplanet atmospheres have been detected, most associated with the so-called 'Hot Jupiters' closest to their stars where sunlight is most intense and the atmospheres extend to the greatest extent due to heating. The most common compounds detected include carbon dioxide and water vapour, but some of the hottest atmospheres contain clouds of vanadium oxide and silicon dioxide in which the rain to their surfaces resembles molten rock. The spectrum of Wasp 19b, located 882 light years from Earth, and orbiting its Sun-like star once every 19 hours, reveals the presence of a hydrocarbon atmosphere containing methane and hydrogen cyanide.

PLANET FORMATION

Since the dust cloud hypothesis for planet formation in a rotating disk of gas was first proposed in 1755, this intuitively simple idea has been tested many times using advanced fluid dynamical calculations on supercomputers and found to be essentially correct. Details have been added such as how the disk would be centrally heated by the evolving protostar. This would produce a temperature gradient decreasing from 2,000 K near the protostar to below 100 K in the outskirts. This temperature gradient allows a variety of chemical reactions to take place, creating various molecules and compounds in equilibrium with their local surroundings. Iron-rich silicate rocks will be common close to the star, while compounds rich in water, ammonia and methane ices will be common at great distances. A planet's composition is determined by where it was formed in this disk. These protoplanetary disks can contain as much as 10 per cent of the mass of the star or more. Massive disks favour the creation of additional stellar companions resulting in binary or trinary star systems. Lower-mass disks favour the creation of planetary and smaller bodies.

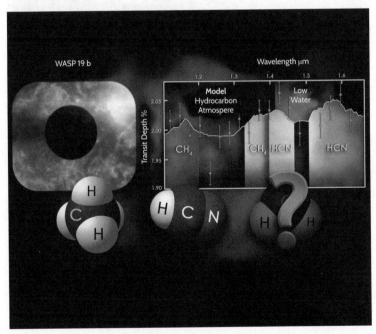

The atmosphere of the exoplanet Wasp 19b. Methane (CH₄) and hydrogen cyanide (HCN) are common ingredients due to the abundance of the constituent elements in the Milky Way. Water (H₂O) appears to be absent in this planet's atmosphere.

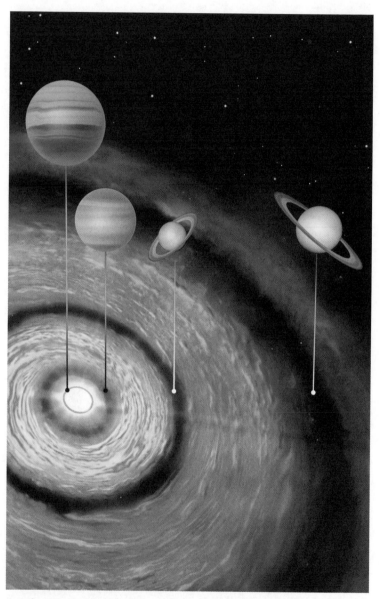

Artist's rendering of ALMA disk and exoplanets near C1 Tauri. The dark lanes are regions where massive forming planets are sweeping out and consuming dust and gas from the disk, making this phase of planet formation visible from Earth.

Astronomers have directly detected many nearby examples of protoplanetary disks, as well as examples of planets actually forming within them. Computer models show that planet-building starts with the accumulation of asteroid-sized bodies into larger masses by a process of low-velocity collisions. As the gravity of the body increases, it can pull in matter from regions far bigger than the geometric size of the body. This begins a very rapid phase of planet-building that ends only when the supply of available gases is reduced. The result will be a massive Jupiter-sized planet located inside an empty ring of disk material, much like what is observed in the HL Tauri and C1 Tauri systems. But these disks can also affect the orbits of these, forming planets through a process of gravitational friction.

Exoplanet studies have been extended to studies of young stellar systems to glean insights into planet formation. The dusty disk of gas surrounding the star HL Tauri was imaged by the Atacama Large Millimeter Array (ALMA) in 2014, revealing a circumstellar disk cut by evacuated rings where planet-building events may be taking place to sweep out the material.

In 2018, astronomer Cathie Clarke used ALMA to image the star C1 Tauri, which is only about 2 million years old. Like HL Tauri, the star is surrounded by a disk of gas and dust, but the inner swept-out zone corresponds to a known Hot Jupiter C1 Tau b (V830 Tau) discovered in 2016 with a 5-day orbit period and a mass of 0.8 Jupiters. The ALMA data also reveals three other gaps further out in the disk, suggesting new massive exoplanets have formed; the farthest one out is at three times the distance of Neptune.

The large number of Hot Jupiters that have been discovered suggests that these massive planets were formed farther out in the disk and over the course of a few million years migrated slowly to their present orbits. The implication of such planetary migration is catastrophic. As they move, they will tend to gravitationally eject any and all smaller bodies they encounter, and disturb the orbits of larger planets. The presence of smaller planets in systems with Hot Jupiters implies that the initial period of planet-building was interrupted by the migrating Jupiters, and any smaller planets now found are second-generation planets. If the disk material can be used up fast enough, this frictional migration can be stopped, freezing the massive Jupiters at large enough distances from the star that they do not have time to interrupt the formation of the smaller interior planets. Based on the number of Hot Jupiter systems, and the location of Jupiter and Saturn as far from our sun as they are, Earth is very fortunate that this planetary migration process came to an end when it did. It also suggests that Jupiter and Saturn were formed at slightly greater distances from the sun than their current locations. Nevertheless, we are fortunate that Jupiter is a member of our solar system. It helped to eject into the Oort Cloud millions of cometary and asteroidal bodies that otherwise would be continuously raining down upon the surfaces of the inner planets even today, possibly making the existence of life impossible.

Key Points

- Planets form by accreting matter from within the orbiting disk of gas and dust surrounding a newly forming star. This process leaves behind dark rings, which are visible from Earth.

- The chemical composition of a planet is determined by where it was formed in this disk, which is very hot near the protostar and very cold at greater distances. This favours ice-rich bodies in the outer solar system and rocky objects closer to the star.

- Massive planets experience friction as they form, which causes their orbits to come closer to the star. This migration process can eject or destroy the smaller earth-sized bodies and form populations of 'Hot Jupiters' close to their stars.

- As an exoplanet passes across the disk of its star as viewed from Earth, the light of its atmosphere can be studied. Compounds such as carbon dioxide and water have been detected in many exoplanet atmospheres.

- Nearly every star in the sky has at least one exoplanet, and small planets such as Earth may be extremely common, numbering in the billions across the Milky Way galaxy.

PART IV
The stars

Chapter 10

Types of Stars

Among the first things astronomers did in studying the stars is similar to what any good zoologist does when encountering a new ecosystem for the first time: You study the properties of individual members and try to put them into a classification scheme. By the early 1900s, astronomers had agreed upon a classification scheme that depended upon the spectroscopic properties of a star, specifically the strength of certain absorption lines of hydrogen (hot stars), calcium (Sun-like stars) and titanium oxide (cool stars) whose changes also followed the temperature of a star.

Stars vary in brightness for two main reasons. In some cases it is because some stars are nearer and some further away, because brightness of an object changes with its distance. Consider, for example, a 100-watt reading lamp. When it is close by it provides very bright illumination at 1 m (3¼ ft), but if you move it five times farther away it will appear much less bright. This is because of a phenomenon known as the *inverse-square law*: the power of a light source is inversely proportional to the square of the distance from the source. So, in the case of the lamp, at 5 m (16½ ft) it will appear 1/25th as bright. However, once distances to stars were determined for a large number of stars, it became apparent that stars vary in their intrinsic luminosity. There are dwarf stars that shine with 1/1000 the power of our Sun and supergiants that are 1 million times more luminous. This led to the construction of a two-dimensional classification scheme for stars that has been in use for over 100 years. Astronomers Ejnar Hertzsprung and Henry Norris Russell were the first to organize stars in this way. The diagrammatic approach they created is called the HR Diagram, which has become one of the most important tools in stellar astronomy.

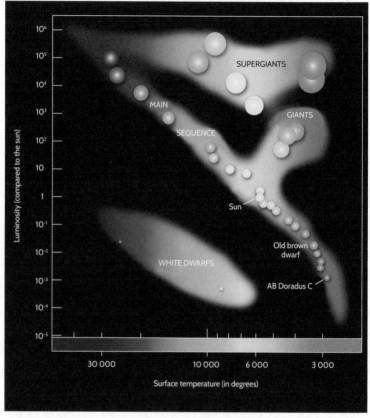

The HR diagram. Supergiant stars can be as large as our entire solar system, while white dwarfs can be similar to Earth in size.

The importance of the HR diagram is that it can be overlain on theoretical models of stellar evolution. Stars of a given mass change positions on this diagram as they evolve from birth to death.

The first thing that astronomers noticed is that the place on the diagram where stars spend most of their time is a diagonal line through the centre. This is called the Main Sequence (MS) and it is here that stars fuse hydrogen into helium as the most abundant form of energy supply. Because stellar lifetimes are measured in billions of years, in any sample of stars, most of them will fall along the MS portion of the diagram. Red giants represent low-mass stars whose cores collapse as they try to ignite helium fusion. Small stars cannot surmount the temperatures needed to trigger helium fusion so they leave the red giant region and end up as dense white dwarf stars having shed most of their atmospheres as *planetary nebulae* (see pages 86–7). Finally we have the supergiants. Massive stars deviate from the MS at high temperatures and move almost horizontally across the top of the diagram to become red supergiants. They can enter and re-enter this region several times as their core nuclear sources pass through the helium-burning, carbon-burning and silicon-burning stages. Eventually, they arrive at the red supergiant class for the last time and subsequently explode as *supernovae* (see page 145).

Another feature of stellar classifications is that luminosity is related to the star's mass. Red dwarf stars (M-dwarfs) that fuse hydrogen must have masses at least 8 per cent the mass of the Sun. O-type MS stars have masses up to 60 times the Sun's mass. In the Milky Way, the most common star is the M-dwarf, while O and B-type stars are rare. For example, in the vicinity of the Sun out to 25 light years, there are 177 stars. Of this sample, 138 are dwarf stars and only 39 are in classes A–K. The dwarf star group can be further divided: 54 of the 138 are brown dwarfs that are too low in mass for hydrogen fusion to occur, and the remaining 84 are M-dwarf stars that do burn hydrogen and are on the MS.

The time it takes a star to critically exhaust its hydrogen reserves can be calculated from detailed theoretical models rather exactly, but there are rules of thumb that can be used to estimate stellar lifetimes such as the equation on the next page, where M is the mass of the star in solar units.

Equation 1) $0.05 < M < 20$ $t = 10^{10}M^{-3.0}$

$0.43 < M < 20$ $t = 10^{10}M^{-2.5}$

$M > 20$ $t = 10^{10}M^{-2}$

For example, a red dwarf star like Wolf 359, located 7.8 light years from the Sun, has a mass of only 0.09 M_{Sun}. From the formula, with M=0.09, its estimated lifespan is about 14 trillion years. Contrast this with the upper Main Sequence star Spica, located 260 light years from the Sun. Its mass is 10.3 M_{Sun} and it has an estimated lifetime of 30 million years.

Astronomers have identified many different sub-categories of stars that in most cases represent transition states in stellar evolution, or are created in response to various environmental factors.

VARIABLE STARS

Although the vast majority of stars produce a constant light output over human timescales, some small numbers of stars vary their light outputs over time scales from hours to years. Although many of these *variable stars* come about because the stars are members of eclipsing binary systems, a significant number are intrinsic variables. This indicates that it is the star itself that is changing its brightness. In fact, variability is a far more common property of stars than previously appreciated. Our own Sun, for example, varies very slightly in ultraviolet output every 11 years due to the presence or absence of sunspots on its surface. This 'microvariability' is very common among Sun-like stars, undoubtedly because sunspots are a very likely feature of stars with magnetic fields and outer convective layers.

For other intrinsic variables, the brightness change comes about from both dramatic physical changes among pulsating variable stars, and from occasional outbursts related to surface magnetic flare activity, common to M-dwarf flare stars.

For pulsating variable stars, the surface of the star undergoes a periodic expansion and contraction. Luminosity is proportional to a star's surface area, so these pulsations cause a dramatic increase in the brightness of the star. The reasons behind this pulsation have to do with the evolution of the star through a region of the HR diagram called the Instability Strip, which represents a set of properties that nearly all stars have as they evolve off the main sequence towards the red giant/supergiant state.

For flare stars, their variability is a feature found among the M-dwarfs such as nearby Proxima Centauri, for which the surface appears to produce intense flares of light very likely similar to solar flares observed on our own Sun. They have their origins in magnetic activity on the surface of a cool, dim star, but the flares are bright enough to dominate the light from the star in a way that solar flares are not able to when observed against the far brighter solar surface.

T-TAURI STARS

These are very young stars less than a few million years old that are found in the vicinity of the dense molecular clouds from which they formed. As nuclear fusion commences in a star, its surface undergoes dramatic changes as the magnetic fields and convection patterns evolve towards a final, stable configuration. During this time, enormous flares erupt and can change the brightness of the star in a complex and erratic manner. This variability can also be detected in the brightness of the protostellar nebula left over from the star's formation.

WOLF–RAYET STARS

These stars typically have masses well above 20 M_{sun}. They produce intense radiation fields that are rich in ultraviolet light due to their surface temperatures being considerably above 50,000 K. These stars produce intense stellar winds driven by radiation pressure. This pressure ejects the outer layers of the star, exposing interior regions where thermonuclear processing and convection yield has enhanced abundances of elements such as helium, carbon, nitrogen and oxygen. Wolf–Rayet stars are the natural evolutionary states of stars more massive than about 50 M_{Sun}. Eventually they end their lives in Type-II supernova explosions. Many of them are found in binary star systems, suggesting that they achieve their large masses by mass transfer from their companion stars.

PECULIAR A-TYPE STARS

About 5 per cent of all stars have very peculiar element abundances at their surfaces. The majority of these are the Ap stars. For normal stars, the surface is well-mixed by convection and low temperatures so that surface abundances reflect more or less the cosmological abundances of elements. For Ap stars, however, their surfaces – or spots on their surfaces – have overabundances of rarer elements such as chromium, strontium and europium. An example is Przybylski's Star, located 355 light years from the Sun in the constellation Centaurus. Its atmosphere shows higher than usual abundances of elements such as strontium, yttrium, praseodymium and uranium. Many of these stars (called Am stars) have extremely strong magnetic fields at their surfaces leading to the idea that these elements are being levitated into separate layers near the surface where convection is being suppressed by the intense magnetic field. However, unusual element abundances are also found in stars that seem to lack strong magnetic fields. The reason for these peculiar rare-earth element abundances remains poorly understood and a one-size-fits-all explanation may not be achievable among the diversity of A-type stars.

Key Points

- Stars come in a variety of types because they have different masses and are seen at different stages in their evolution.

- The lifespan of a star is determined by its mass, with stars like our Sun able to last about 13 billion years, but more massive stars can survive only a few million years, and dwarf stars with 10 per cent of the sun's mass can last for trillions of years.

- The most massive stars are intense sources of ultraviolet radiation and can ionize all the interstellar hydrogen gas surrounding them out to tens of light years' distance.

- Stars in the T-Tauri class are similar in mass to our Sun but are less than 10 million years old, providing us with a glimpse into what our Sun looked like in its infancy.

- Variable stars are a common phase of stellar evolution as a star evolves into a red giant. An instability arises in the nuclear heating that causes the star to rhythmically expand and contract over the course of days or years.

Chapter 11

Star Formation

Stars are spheres of heated plasma with core densities of 100 g/cc or higher. By contrast, the interstellar medium (ISM) is a dilute collection of gas and clouds that occupies the space between the stars in the Milky Way with an average gas density of about 1 atom/cc. Somehow the ISM has to be concentrated by a factor of 10^{30} in order to form a star. Based on studies of many star-forming sites within the interstellar clouds in the Milky Way, it seems that the manner in which this concentration occurs is via gravitational collapse. The specific end products of this collapse depend on the mass of the final star, so astronomers consider stellar evolution according to four mass ranges: brown dwarfs, normal stars, massive stars and hypergiant stars.

Although stars range in brightness from 0.0001 to 10 million times the Sun's (solar) output – a factor of 100 trillion in range – their masses only span 200 solar masses to 0.003 solar masses – a range of 100,000. Each mass range leads to a different formation environment and evolution outcome.

BROWN DWARF STARS

The lowest-mass objects that can sustain thermonuclear fusion temperatures are the brown dwarf stars with masses above about 80 times the mass of Jupiter. Objects below this mass are not able to burn lithium as the lowest-temperature fusion process. SDSS

J0104+1535 is the most massive brown dwarf known and is 90 times more massive than Jupiter. At some point, the masses of brown dwarfs reach the typical sizes of red dwarf stars with 8 per cent the mass of the Sun (80 Jupiters). The brown dwarf masses range from 3–10 times that of Jupiter for Y-dwarfs in the case of WISE 0825, to 33 Jupiters in the case of the L-dwarf Luhman 16A. Although Luhman 16A shines with a steady light, its smaller T-dwarf companion Luhman 16B has a variable light output implying a cloudy atmosphere. L-dwarfs are not hot enough for lithium to fuse, hence the name L-dwarfs. T-dwarfs are cool enough that methane clouds form in their atmospheres and can be easily detected using the light they give off in the infrared spectrum at wavelengths of 2-microns. Epsilon Indi Ba and Bb are both T-dwarfs with masses of 45 and 27 Jupiters.

Initially, it was thought that brown dwarfs form in much the same way as planets, through condensation in a protoplanetary disk orbiting a young star. However, recent direct detection of brown dwarfs forming in a nearby molecular cloud in the

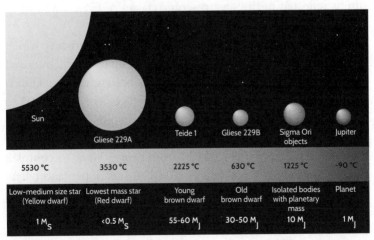

Sun	Gliese 229A	Teide 1	Gliese 229B	Sigma Ori objects	Jupiter
5530 °C	3530 °C	2225 °C	630 °C	1225 °C	-90 °C
Low-medium size star (Yellow dwarf)	Lowest mass star (Red dwarf)	Young brown dwarf	Old brown dwarf	Isolated bodies with planetary mass	Planet
$1\,M_S$	$<0.5\,M_S$	$55\text{-}60\,M_J$	$30\text{-}50\,M_J$	$10\,M_J$	$1\,M_J$

Brown dwarf surface temperatures and relative sizes. The masses relative to multiples of Jupiter (M_J) and the sun (M_S) are also indicated. Objects cooler than 2000°C (3632°F) are extremely bright infrared sources and easily detectable at these wavelengths.

constellation Taurus shows that these objects develop directly from the gravitational collapse of cold gas within dense clouds, similar to the way ordinary stars form. The Taurus brown dwarfs are observed to have jets of matter, which are not found in giant planet formation from a disk. For some reason, some interstellar clouds lead to gravitational collapse of pre-stellar masses that are very small. Nevertheless, the abundance of similarities between red dwarf stars and brown dwarfs implies that brown dwarfs are simply smaller versions of ordinary stars and form in the same way through a process similar to simple gravitational collapse and disk formation that otherwise shows no mass scale favouritism.

NORMAL STARS

Beginning with the red dwarf stars with masses of 8 per cent that of the Sun, and surface temperatures near 3,500 K, normal stars make up the vast majority of known stars leading to the massive A-type stars nearly twice the mass of the Sun and surface temperatures of 10,000 K. The sequence of stars ordered by temperature is reflected in the spectroscopic classes A, F, G, K and M in decreasing temperature.

These 'normal' stars have a similar formation process, which starts with cold molecular clouds with sizes up to several hundred light years and masses up to 100,000 solar masses. These clouds have temperatures below 100 K, and average densities of 100 to 1,000 atoms/cc. The composition of these clouds varies from the surface, where simple molecules abound in the presence of the interstellar radiation field (ISRF) from nearby stars, to complex molecules such as formaldehyde (CH_4) and cyanopentaacetylene ($HC_{11}N$) formed in the dense cold cores opaque to the ISRF. Cloud interiors can be in a state of rotation and possess magnetic fields, and also undergo turbulent motion, which can serve to support some or all of the cloud against gravitational collapse for extended periods of times measured in millions of years.

At some point, this dynamic equilibrium becomes disturbed and gravitational collapse ensues. Higher density cloud regions collapse faster than lower density regions. Turbulence tends to follow a declining spectrum of size scales as energy is being dissipated through friction, leading to a range of cell masses, which in turn can become gravitationally unstable and collapse. As they do, their rotational angular momentum is conserved and the collapsing cells become increasingly flattened disks. Since dense regions collapse faster than less dense ones, the centres of these disks form dense collapsing proto-stellar cores millions of kilometres across, embedded within circulating disks of protoplanetary matter.

As the protostar continues to collapse, gravitational potential energy is converted into kinetic energy that becomes randomized by collisions. This causes the temperature of the protostar to increase. The core of the protostar reaches temperatures high enough to ionize the material in the core. The thermal pressure from the rising plasma temperatures causes the gravitational collapse to slow down but not stop. The infalling gas has been

Artist's rendering of a T-Tauri star. The central proto-star is orbited by a dense disk of gas, dust and asteroidal material from which planets may eventually form.

transparent to its own radiation so that little radiation pressure is produced. However, once the material becomes dense enough to be opaque to its own radiation, the thermal and radiation pressure is finally able to balance the pressure from the infalling matter and gravitational collapse stops. This also corresponds to the time when the core temperature reaches 15 million K where thermonuclear fusion can commence. At this time the protostar has become a star; however, the dynamics of this time remain very complex beyond the surface (*photosphere*) of the star.

As the protostar forms, the infalling matter has also transported powerful magnetic fields to the protostar's surface. These strongly interact with the hot plasma now occupying the surface of the star. The fields have a complex magnetic configuration, and reconnect themselves into simpler dipolar geometries producing enormous stellar flares and an intense stellar wind. These events produce powerful radio and X-ray emissions and a complex pattern of optical variability, and this is how they can be detected by

Herbig Haro 46/47 is a young star ejecting matter into two jets, which are identified as two 'Herbig-Haro Objects'. The proto-stars are often heavily obscured by the circumstellar disk, with the jets streaming away along the polar axis of the disk

astronomers. Having conserved angular momentum as it formed, the star is a very rapid rotator at hundreds of km/s, but the magnetic field connection between the star and the circumstellar disk acts as a brake to this rotation. Over time the star slows to a rotation speed of only a few km/s. This activity also creates jets of matter ejected along the rotation axis of the disk, which also dissipate energy back into the molecular cloud, increasing the internal energy and turbulence.

When many protostars form in a molecular cloud, they can ultimately become members of a bound star cluster if the amount of cloud mass converted into stars is very large. If few stars are formed and a significant cloud mass is left behind, the stars will not be gravitationally bound and so the stars will move independently through space. Within the nearby Orion Nebula, over 1000 young, X-ray emitting stars have been detected. Globular star clusters have tens of thousands of stars of about half a solar mass, formed in a volume of space a few dozen light years across. These clusters formed over 10 billion years ago when the formation efficiency of the environment was far higher than is currently found within the Milky Way today. Star formation currently proceeds at a pace of 0.7 to 1.4 solar masses/year within the entire Milky Way. It is very inefficient with lots of cloud mass left over.

The Taurus Molecular Cloud is the closest star-forming cloud to our Sun, at a distance of only 430 light years. The cloud is filled with an intricate network of dense filaments, and the current star-forming activity appears to be confined to nodes in these filaments. The magnetic fields tend to be perpendicular to these filaments and aligned with features called striations that may be funnelling matter to make the filaments grow in mass. Over 40 dense cores have been detected, each about 0.3 light years in diameter and between 1 and 10 solar masses. The amount of ultraviolet light is very low in these dark clouds, so the forming stars are not able to ionize the hydrogen in the molecular cloud at distances much beyond the scale of the circumstellar disks themselves. That means that star formation in this mass range is relatively gentle and may not preclude many low-mass stars from forming at the same time.

MASSIVE 'OB' STARS

At the highest end of the mass range for normal stars are the spectroscopic O and B-type stars with masses from 3 to 50 times the mass of the Sun. Although they also form from the gravitational collapse of molecular cloud cores, they have a dramatic impact on the structure and star-forming activity across many light years of interstellar space.

Once the protostar stabilizes as a fully-fledged star with 15,000 K to 50,000 K surface temperature, its ultraviolet output

The nearby and famous Orion Nebula HII region, which is a stellar nursery rich in massive stars that emit copious quantities of ultraviolet light and ionize the surrounding gas, causing it to glow.

is so intense that it can ionize the hydrogen gas out to many light years, forming what astronomers call an 'HII Region'. HI is the spectroscopic name for neutral hydrogen, while HII indicates the hydrogen atom has lost its single electron. These HII regions are among the most beautiful objects in the universe. The nearest one to our Sun is the Orion Nebula at a distance of 1,300 light years.

HYPERGIANT STARS

These stars are rare and represent perhaps only a few thousand examples in an entire galaxy like the Milky Way. Their masses range from 50 to 150 times that of our Sun. Like massive stars, they form from molecular clouds, but soon after the circumstellar disk has established itself, the protostar turns on very quickly. The enormous ultraviolet radiation flux acts upon the inflowing material to ionize it. This is easiest done along the poles of the young star, and hardest in the equatorial plane. The resulting radiation pressure reverses the polar flow into bipolar outflows at very high velocity. In the equatorial plane, matter continues to flow into the star as an accretion flow at a rate of about 0.001 solar masses/year. This quickly allows the star to achieve enormous masses exceeding 100 solar masses. The process ends when the radiation pressure from the star is able to quench the flow. What is not fully understood is why some molecular cloud cores fragment into clusters of OB stars, while others develop into single hyperstars. One theoretical model suggests that hyperstars may grow by the merger of OB stars in very small clusters, much like galaxies grow in mass by cannibalizing their neighbours during collision events.

The most massive hyperstar, R136A1, is located in the Tarantula Nebula in the Large Magellanic Cloud some 160,000 light years from the Sun. The star has an estimated mass greater that 300 Suns at the time of formation. Over 31 stars are known to have masses above 100 solar masses. The closest hyperstar with a mass of 110 times that of our Sun is Cygnus OB2-12, located at a distance of 5,500 light years. It is 2 million times more luminous than our Sun.

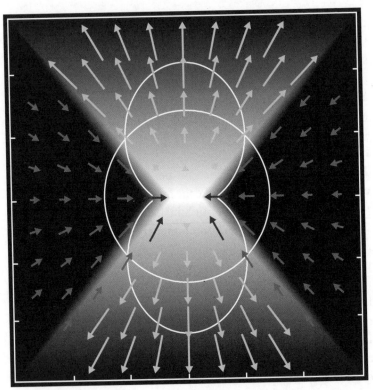

Calculated equatorial inflow and polar outflows in a massive star. Gas flows into the circumstellar disk (inward-pointing arrows) and is directed into polar outflows through the action of magnetic fields within the inner disk and growing proto-star core.

Key Points

- Stars form from collapsing interstellar gas clouds by a specific process that is still not fully understood.

- The mass of a forming protostar determines whether its core will become hot enough for thermonuclear fusion to occur, and how vigorously these reactions will heat the star's core.

- The threshold for forming a star is about 80 times the mass of Jupiter. Below this mass, temperatures are too cool for thermonuclear reactions to occur and the matter becomes a degenerate solid.

- Stars that are ten times the mass of our Sun, called OB stars, are copious producers of ultraviolet light and produce spectacular, glowing nebulae.

- Stars can grow by mergers to become very massive, with the most massive, called hypergiant stars, having over 100 times the mass of our Sun.

Chapter 12

Stellar Evolution

The biggest driver of stellar evolution is the mass of the star. This determines the core temperature via the conversion of gravitational potential energy into thermal energy, and this in turn sharply determines the luminosity of the star. There are three basic relationships, or equations, for stellar evolution. These equations use the Sun as a unit of measurement, so M is the star's mass in multiples of our Sun's mass and L is the star's luminosity in multiples of the Sun's luminosity. The Sun's mass is $M_{Sun}=2\times10^{30}$ kg (M=1.0) and $L_{Sun}=4\times10^{26}$ watts (L=1.0). The temperature (T) is the star's surface temperature. For the Sun, a typical 'yellow' star, T=5770 K.

The first equation describes how the luminosity of a star depends on its surface temperature and radius:

Equation 1)
Luminosity Law: $L = 8.6 \times 10^{-16}R^2T^4$

The second equation relates the luminosity of a star to its mass and takes into account that objects within the different mass groups – dwarf star, main sequence star, massive star – behave somewhat differently as their sources of internal energy change:

Equation 2)

Luminosity

Dwarf:	$M < 0.43M$	$L = 0.23M^{2.3}$
Main Sequence:	$0.43 < M < 20$	$L = M^4$
Massive:	$M > 55$	$L = 32000\,M$

This final equation relates the available mass of the star in nuclear fuel to the luminosity of the star to give an estimate of the star's lifetime as it burns hydrogen to helium on the Main Sequence (MS):

Equation 3)

MS Lifetime

Dwarf:	$0.05 < M < 0.43$	$t = 10^{10}M^{-3.0}$
Main Sequence:	$0.43 < M < 20$	$t = 10^{10}M^{-2.5}$
Massive:	$M > 20$	$t = 10^{10}M^{-2}$

The bright star Betelgeuse has a mass of 20 M_{Sun} ($M=20$) and a surface temperature of $T=3,500$ K. From Equation 1, its radius R is about 1,100 $R_{Suns.}$ Equation 3 its estimated life as a main sequence star is six million years. These properties make this star a red supergiant.

The Main Sequence (MS) lifetime is the longest evolutionary phase that a star experiences during which time it is fusing the most abundant element: hydrogen. Eventually it 'evolves off' the MS as it approaches its end of life. Our Sun arrived on the MS about 4.5 billion years ago and so, with an MS lifespan of 12 billion years, it has another 7.5 billion years to go before hydrogen fusion becomes fuel-starved and our Sun evolves dramatically. For red dwarf stars like Proxima Centauri, with masses of 0.12 M_{Sun}, this MS time can be 6 trillion years. For massive stars like Rigel, with $M=19$ M_{Sun}, the MS time can be as short as 6 million years. Exactly what happens to a star as it evolves off the Main Sequence depends entirely upon its mass.

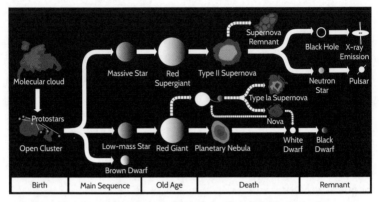

A graphical summary of the major stages in stellar evolution from the collapse of interstellar dust clouds (left side) through the various stages and astronomical objects that result depending on the mass of the star.

BROWN DWARF STARS (0.08 TO 0.3 M$_{SUN}$)

These stars have insufficient mass to fuse hydrogen into helium. Because of their low mass, the only support they have against gravitational collapse is via electrostatic repulsion between constituent ions and atoms. This is the same 'solid body' force that keeps the atoms in the chair you are sitting on from collapsing into a dense ball of nuclear matter. This inter-atomic, electrostatic repulsion limits their sizes to about that of Jupiter, so their evolution is similar to the evolution of massive, gas-rich planets like Jupiter. As these objects cool, they undergo gravitational contraction to still smaller radii over time. Initially, these 'failed stars' may be held up by simple thermal 'heat' pressure but very quickly the core of the object under its high pressure becomes what is called a *degenerate plasma*. Electrons are forced out from their atoms and become a new type of gas whose properties are limited by quantum mechanics. At most two electrons (with opposite spins) can be in the same energy/momentum quantum state. If a plasma reaches the point in pressure and density where all the electron quantum states are completely filled, no further density change can occur. Under these degeneracy conditions, even gravitational collapse cannot overcome the quantum rigidity of this electron plasma and so the object ceases to contract forever. From this time onwards, the object steadily gives up its internal thermal energy and evolves over the course of trillions of years into a solid, cold object at near absolute zero.

MAIN SEQUENCE STARS (0.4 TO 2 M_{SUN})

These stars span the spectral classes from red dwarf M-type stars to very hot A-type stars. The evolution of these stars is extremely complex because as hydrogen fuels become insufficient to prevent gravitational collapse, other nuclear fuels step in as the core temperature increases to alter the progress of evolution. Also, the primary source of energy generation can move temporarily from the core to fuel-rich zones surrounding the core. This also changes the structure and size of the star. The stars in this mass range represent the vast majority of the stars in the Milky Way and evolve in roughly the same way, though the details depend very sensitively on the mass of the star.

When the abundance of hydrogen fuel in the core is depleted by about 20 per cent, the star has already grown slightly in luminosity and size because the steady collapse of the core heats it up and so the fusion reactions run more vigorously. This causes the star to slowly expand. Eventually, the region surrounding the core reaches the triggering temperature for fusion and, from this time forward, hydrogen 'shell burning' starts to produce more energy than the core so the star begins to expand rapidly and its outer layers cool. The star has now become an evolving red giant, and will steadily grow in radius and luminosity as its surface temperature remains roughly constant. Meanwhile, these reactions continue to shower the core region with inert helium 'ash', which is a by-product of hydrogen fusion. The massive ash core increases in temperature through gravitational collapse until it is possible for three helium nuclei to fuse into a carbon nucleus, a process called the triple-alpha reaction.

For stars in this mass range, the triple-alpha reaction is triggered in a core of matter that is being held up by electron degeneracy pressure. Such a gas does not behave the same way as ordinary gases because instead of the pressure increasing as it is heated, the pressure remains exactly the same as the core heats up. The triple-alpha reaction is triggered literally in a flash, but all this does is to remove the degeneracy effect so the core can temporarily behave as a normal gas. Nevertheless, this has little effect on the star as a whole. With helium burning in the core and hydrogen burning in the shell region, the star has reached its largest size as a red giant. From now on, as the helium is depleted in the core, and with no further fusion sources available to it, the core returns to a degenerate state and the star dramatically contracts in size. Eventually, it will lose its outer layers as a planetary nebula, with only its dense hot degenerate, carbon-rich core left behind as a dim 'white dwarf' no larger than our Earth.

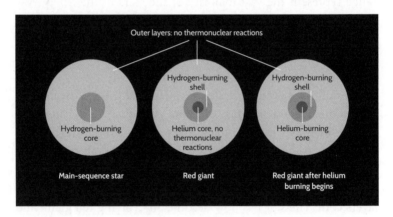

Interior of low-mass star post-MS, which follows the red giant stages through the event known as the helium flash, where three helium are fused to make a single carbon nucleus.

MASSIVE STARS (3 M$_{SUN}$ TO 50 M$_{SUN}$)

These stars are classified as O- and B-type stars and have far more dramatic evolutionary histories. Like the lower-mass stars, they too will deplete their hydrogen fuel reserves, expanding and cooling to become red giants, but by the time core temperatures reach the triple-alpha ignition temperature of about 300 million K, their core regions are not degenerate. The helium burning phase occurs far more gently and the star expands to become a red supergiant. As helium ash is converted to carbon in the core, the shell-burning region also contributes to expanding the star. These stars can be so vast that they would occupy the entire solar system out to the orbit of Neptune.

As the helium ash becomes steadily depleted from conversion into carbon, the core collapses and heats, allowing carbon to be fused into a steadily increasing list of heavier elements thanks to the availability and growing abundances of helium nuclei, and other lower-mass nuclei which can now participate in fusion reactions. With each change, the core grows hotter and the shell-burning layers outside the nucleus become more complex. In fact, the interior becomes a multi-shelled energy production environment with the hydrogen-burning shell being the farthest from the core, followed by a helium-burning shell, a carbon-burning shell and so on. With each change, the star temporarily decreases in luminosity while its surface temperature increases slightly. Then, as the new shell-burning reaction takes over, it

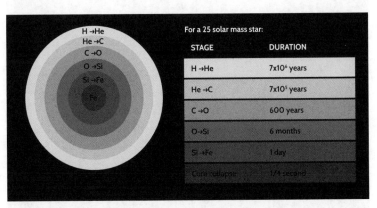

For a 25 solar mass star:

STAGE	DURATION
H →He	7x10⁶ years
He →C	7x10⁵ years
C →O	600 years
O→Si	6 months
Si →Fe	1 day
Core collapse	1/4 second

A star's interior just before supernova explosion for a star 25 times the mass of the Sun. The core undergoes many changes as it converts hydrogen nuclei into iron nuclei through a series of intermediate stages lasting progressively shorter times.

again rises back into the domain of the red supergiant. Eventually, as the availability of new nuclei to fuse diminishes, the reactions reach a critical point for the most massive stars.

For the low end of this mass range, the amount of material in the core is comparable to the mass of our Sun. At the same time that the nuclear reactions have been producing gamma-rays that heat the interior, they also produce neutrinos, which escape from the interior within minutes and do not contribute to providing internal pressure. By the time the temperatures become high enough so that iron nuclei become abundant fusion by-products, continued core collapse no longer increases the core energy but instead

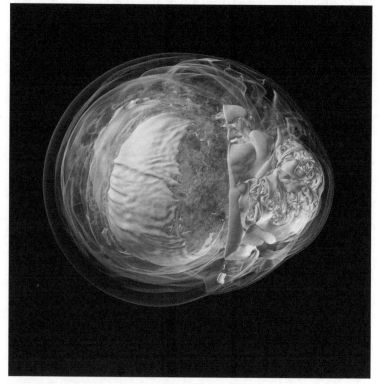

Computer simulation of the complex gas motions in a detonating star. The complex layering in the core results from variations in the temperature and entropy of the plasma leading to an onion-like stratification.

The famous Crab supernova of 1054 CE and its nebula.

becomes a mechanism for fragmenting the iron nuclei by gamma-ray interactions. This process, like the neutrino emission, causes substantial energy to be lost from the core and so gravitational collapse begins and overcomes the restraining pressure. As the core region becomes denser and denser within a few minutes of infall, the enormous luminosity of neutrinos becomes suddenly trapped by the dramatic increase in density to near-nuclear levels. This happens so suddenly that this pressure spike causes the star to explode as a 'Type-II' supernova. Meanwhile, the 'equal and opposite force' causes the core to become compressed.

Lower-mass stars in this range, those with masses between 10 and 30 M_{Sun}, leave behind neutron stars. Below 10 M_{Sun} they become white dwarfs. But above 30 M_{Sun} not even the degeneracy pressure provided by neutrons (quarks) can prevent further collapse, so the supernova remnants continue to collapse until they become black holes (see page 134). This rearrangement happens literally within a few minutes after the star detonates.

The out-flowing plasma is incredibly dense and turbulent. Computer models show that in the brief seconds that this nuclear plasma exists, it creates nearly all the elements in the periodic table. Earlier studies were concerned that this enriched material would recollapse and never be mixed with the interstellar medium. However, modern calculations show that the neutrino pressure is more than sufficient to detonate the star, allowing enormous quantities of matter to reach escape velocity. The most important added factor that made the calculations predict a full detonation of the star was contributed by the electroweak theory developed by physicists Steven Weinberg, Abdus Salam and Howard Georgi in the late 1960s. It was known that the luminosity and energy loss by pre-supernova stars through neutrino emission was gargantuan and of the order of five times the luminosity of our Sun. But neutrinos hardly interact at all with matter so they were unable to deliver this energy to take part in the detonation of the star. What electroweak theory predicted is that there should be a neutral, weak interaction between neutrinos and matter. This turned out to be the missing ingredient. When it was added to the dynamics of the collapsing supernova core, as the density of matter approached nuclear densities, the neutral weak interaction delivered a sudden pulse of new energy and pressure that countered the collapse. But its pressure was so great that it almost instantly pushed the infalling matter outwards with enough energy to cause detonation and the ejection of tens of solar masses of matter into interstellar space.

NEUTRON STARS

Under high-enough pressure, electrons in a dense plasma can be forced to react with protons to form neutrons. At densities

THE DISCOVERY OF PULSARS

Jocelyn Bell Burnell is an Irish astrophysicist who discovered the first pulsar in 1967 as a piece of 'scruff' on her data recorder, which had a pulse interval of 1.5 seconds. The radio source was called B1919+21, or also 'Little Green Man-1' due to its seemingly artificial nature. Later called a 'pulsar', this discovery opened the door on investigating neutron stars and their environments. She was awarded the 2018 Special Breakthrough Prize in Physics but donated the $3 million award 'to fund women, under-represented ethnic minority and refugee students to become physics researchers'.

approaching nuclear matter, 10^{14} g/cc, this material forms neutronized matter consisting of about 5 per cent protons and electrons with 95 per cent as pure neutrons. Like the white dwarfs supported by electron degeneracy pressure, neutrons also produce a quantum degeneracy pressure that stabilizes the object against further collapse. Unlike electron degeneracy pressure mediated by the electromagnetic force, the neutron degeneracy pressure involves the strong nuclear force and the object stabilizes at a size that is 1,000 times smaller than a white dwarf, or about 20 km (12½ miles) across. The object has conserved angular momentum

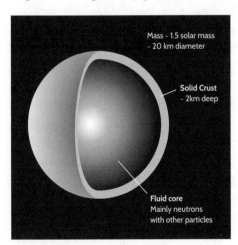

Mass – 1.5 solar mass
~ 20 km diameter

Solid Crust
~ 2km deep

Fluid core
Mainly neutrons
with other particles

Basic interior structure of a neutron star 20 km (12½ miles) in diameter.

following the supernova explosion and can be rotating hundreds of times a second. The crust is a thin 1 m (3 ft) layer of dense plasma and magnetic fields, which can emit pulses of radio, optical and X-ray energy detectable by astronomers as 'pulsar' emission.

Only 5 per cent of the star's mass consists of electrons and protons, which form a crust less than 2 km (1¼ miles) thick. This crust is subject to 'starquakes', which can be observed from Earth as glitches in pulsar radio signals.

There may be as many as 100 million neutron stars in the Milky Way. Only 2,000 are known, primarily because these spinning objects produce pulses of radio radiation that is detectable if aimed directly towards our planet where it can be detected by Earth-based receivers and are therefore called pulsars.

BLACK HOLES

The most massive stable neutron star has a theoretical mass of 3.0 M_{Sun} and could be produced by a star with under 20 M_{Sun} if most of its mass is lost during the supernova phase. For stars leaving behind remnant masses greater than this, the object cannot be stabilized by neutron degeneracy pressure and continues to collapse to become a *black hole*. These objects have such intense gravitational fields light cannot escape from them and hence would be black to a distant observer. They also distort the geometry of space and time in their vicinity, leading to many complicated effects. Black holes were predicted by Albert Einstein's 1915 theory of general relativity, and their properties are completely defined by three numbers: mass (M), angular momentum (L), charge (Q). If they are not spinning so that L=0, they are called Schwarzschild black holes and for them their critical radius, called the event horizon, is given by the simple formula R = 2.9 M km, where M is in M_{Sun} units. For a remnant the mass of our sun, its event horizon would be at a distance of only 2.9 km (1¾ miles) from its centre.

In almost all cases for young supernovae, the black hole will be at least temporarily surrounded by an *accretion disk,* that is, a collection of material brought together by the influence of gravity and forming a disk around the black hole. If the black hole is part of a binary star system, this disk can also be formed over time by accreting material from the nearby star. The emission from this disk makes it a very strong X-ray source. These can be distinguished from accretion disks that may form around neutron stars by the energy of the X-rays. Black hole disks are at higher temperature and can produce higher energy (or 'hard') X-rays than is the case for neutron stars, which produce lower energy (or 'soft') X-rays.

Currently there are 18 known stellar-massed black holes. The closest is V616 Monocerotis with a mass of 11 M_{Sun}, located 3,500 light years from the Sun. Estimates suggest that millions of black holes may exist in our Milky Way, but are currently not being 'fed' by the accreting interstellar matter necessary to make them detectable.

An accretion disk around a black hole will appear visually distorted due to the bending of light by the warped space near the event horizon.

HYPERSTARS (> 50 M$_{Sun}$)

The relationship between mass and lifetime undergoes a huge change for stars with masses above 100 M$_{Sun}$. Within less than 1 million years, the star exhausts its hydrogen and during the next million years or so reaches the point where a supernova explosion takes place. This timescale is so rapid that these stars are almost always found inside or close by the giant molecular clouds out of which they formed. The star may be deeply embedded in the cloud and not even visible at optical wavelengths but can be detected as an intense ultra-luminous infrared 'star'. If it has broken out of its cloud, it is accompanied by a vast HII region.

Hyperstars continue, and amplify, the trend found in the most massive O-type stars (M=20 M$_{Sun}$). The amount of light

An artist's rendering of the break-out of a gamma-ray beam. This event can be observed from Earth as a GRB if the beams are pointed in exactly the right direction.

emitted by their surfaces is so intense that the pressure of radiation is capable of pushing back at the incoming material. The outer layers of hydrogen have been ejected by the radiation pressure producing intense stellar winds. These stars are known as Wolf–Rayet stars, and their surfaces are rich in helium and carbon convected to the surface from the interior shell-burning zones. Surface temperatures exceed 100,000 K. As powerful ultraviolet sources, they ionize huge volumes of the interstellar medium, provided they are not too embedded in dense cloud material. About 500 of these stars have been found in our own galaxy, and they are among the easiest stars to identify in other galaxies. Wolf–Rayet galaxies have so many of these stars that the light from the galaxy looks like that of a normal WR star.

What remains behind after a hyperstar's supernova depends on its mass. Below about 150 M_{Sun}, their cores collapse to black holes within a rapidly expanding supernova shell. Between about 150 and 250 M_{Sun}, a powerful instability occurs in the oxygen-fusing core. The gamma-ray photons are energetic and numerous enough to produce matter–antimatter pairs. This ultimately leads to a detonation that completely destroys the core of the star, leaving nothing behind as a remnant. For masses more than about 250 M_{Sun}, the matter–antimatter pair-production instability is not energetic enough to destroy the core. Instead, we end up with another phenomenon: gamma-ray bursts.

As the core region implodes, some may be in a state of rapid rotation so that leading up to the explosion event the core resembles a central core surrounded by a rotating disk of matter. The density of this matter is at near-nuclear densities. When the core collapse event occurs, a massive black hole forms within milliseconds, and the rotating disk of matter acts to 'focus' (collimate) a powerful jet of particles along the poles of the rotating disk. This pair of beams blasts through the dense plasma within the body of the star and erupts at the star's surface, producing a powerful pulse or 'burst' of gamma-ray light. The beams may erupt in two opposite directions. If Earth is along the axis of one of these beams, spacecraft will detect a burst of gamma-ray light even when the source is billions of light years distant. Astronomers believe that this is the most likely mechanism for producing the gamma-ray bursts (GRBs) that have been detected all across the sky, since they were first discovered by the Vela military reconnaisance satellites in the 1960s. GRBs are detected among the most distant galaxies in our visible universe, and appear about once every day. Some calculations suggest that up to half the explosion energy can be converted into beams of gamma-rays.

Hyperstars can have masses up to 300 M_{Sun} and are very rare within spiral and irregular galaxies in which star formation can take place. At a distance of 2 billion light years, GRB 030329 is the closest GRB detected. The closest potential GRB hyperstar is R136a1 with a mass estimated at 315 M_{Sun}. It is located in the Tarantula Nebula in the Large Magellanic Cloud about 160,000 light years from the Sun. This 'front row seat' on the evolution of a potential GRB progenitor would be of some concern if Earth were located along the rotation axis of R136a1, which fortunately it is not. The GRB beam that will some day travel along this axis and into the depths of the universe would be capable of ionizing the atmosphere of Earth even at this distance, causing the instant extinction of life on Earth.

Key Points

- The mass of a star determines how it will evolve, how long this process will take, and the luminosity of the star.

- The lowest-mass stars, called Brown Dwarfs, have masses between 0.08 and 0.3 times the sun's mass and fuse hydrogen into helium so slowly that they can sustain this process for trillions of years.

- Stars like our sun evolve to become white dwarfs and planetary nebula within tens of billions of years.

- Stars with higher masses become supernovae and leave behind neutron stars or black holes depending on whether their masses are below or above about 20 solar masses.

- The most massive stars with upwards of 100 solar masses evolve in only a few million years into supernovae, which can produce gamma ray bursts visible for billions of light years across the universe.

PART V
The Galaxy

Chapter 13

Galactic Structure

By the start of the 20th century, the development of powerful telescopes combined with the advent of more sensitive photographic film provided the technological resources to study the detailed shapes of 'extragalactic nebulae'. In a process reminiscent of biological classification schemes, the shapes of certain nebulae – later to be called 'galaxies' – were classified into common families with evocative names such as 'spirals', 'ellipticals', 'barred-spirals' and 'irregulars'. In 1926, the astronomer Edwin Hubble offered his 'Hubble Sequence' (or, as it became known, the 'Hubble Tuning Fork Diagram') as a way to organize the shapes. It was not intended to represent an evolutionary

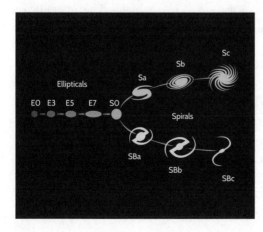

The Hubble classifications were developed in the late 1920s as a means of organizing the shapes of galaxies into specific types, which were thought to form an evolutionary sequence from young ellipticals to older spirals.

scheme; ellipticals did not 'evolve' into spirals, for example. Nevertheless, ellipticals are sometimes called 'early-type' galaxies and spirals 'late-type' galaxies as a holdover from this early time. To further understand why there are such specific morphological types, we need to understand the structure of individual galaxies and the environments in which they developed.

Within the Milky Way, spectroscopic studies begun by Walter Baade in the 1940s had revealed several different populations of stars. These stars are distinguished by the abundance of elements heavier than helium, which for historical reasons are referred to as 'metals'. Because iron is an easy spectral line to detect, the metallicity index denoted by Z is generally the ratio of the iron abundance to the hydrogen abundance. Population I (Pop I) stars have 'high metallicities' (they are metal-rich) approaching the 4 per cent measured in recently-formed stars. Our Sun ($Z=0.013$) is a Pop I star. Population II (Pop II) stars are metal-poor stars with less than 0.1 per cent of their mass in metals. The metallicity of a star also relates to its location within the Milky Way.

The famous Pleiades cluster in the constellation Taurus contains Pop I stars less than 115 million years old. The majority of the bright stars are massive B-type stars.

Among the Pop I stars you will find very young stars of all masses that have formed relatively recently in the roughly 13-billion-year history of our galaxy. These stars are generally found very close to the disk plane of the Milky Way, and among the star-forming clouds. Open star clusters, for example, are generally rich in Pop I stars, having been formed in the last few hundred million years or so. In contrast, Pop II stars have only traces of heavy elements and are found in globular clusters and in the distant halo of the Milky Way. There are also populations of stars that have intermediate metallicities, such as the 'nuclear bulge' population and the so-called 'thick-disk' population. These are, nevertheless, more similar to Pop II stars than to Pop I stars. The distribution of these stellar populations in the Milky Way provides insights into their ages and the evolution of the Milky Way itself.

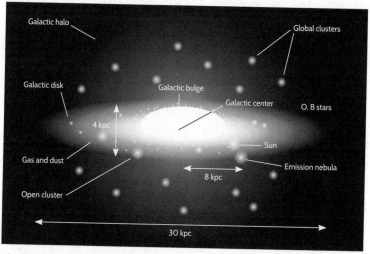

The basic structure of the Milky Way. Each of these components traces a unique population of stars from older Pop-II halo stars to the very young Pop I stars still found within interstellar dust cloud nurseries.

Beginning with a primordial population of Pop III stars, which were composed of pure hydrogen and helium, these massive stars became supernovae within a few million years and scattered enriched gas into space. Pop II stars formed from this enriched gas and became the stars we see today in the Milky Way's halo and nuclear bulge regions. Although Pop II stars have incredibly low quantities of metals, there are none that have zero metals. Also, these Pop II stars tend to have masses below that of our Sun. The oldest measured age for a Pop II star is 12.8 billion years for Chaffau's Star (SDSS J102915+172927) located 4,500 light years from the Sun in the galactic halo in the direction of constellation Leo. The Milky Way has over 160 globular star clusters that are found in the halo region and orbit the galactic centre bulge. These are also Pop II systems with ages between 10 and 13 billion years. The implication is that the halo formed first, followed by the globular clusters. The disk of the Milky Way is the youngest component and is still forming stars today.

Based on this information, spectroscopic studies of elliptical galaxies show that they are almost exclusively Pop II star systems, indicating that they formed at about the same time as the Milky Way's halo. According to the Hubble Classifications, elliptical galaxies are indeed 'early-type' galaxies: 'early' in the sense that they formed soon after the Big Bang. Studies of the dynamics of elliptical galaxies show that the various types along the Hubble Sequence are mixtures of other ellipticals seen at different viewing angles. Lenticular forms such as the E8 can look like E0 galaxies when viewed face-on.

SPIRAL ARMS

Although elliptical galaxies are essentially devoid of interstellar gases and clouds, spiral and irregular galaxies can contain up to 20 per cent of their total mass in this material between the stars. The behaviour of this gas leads to many important morphological features. The most dramatic spiral galaxy features are the arms themselves. The gas disks do not rotate as a solid body but spin at faster speeds at their centres than at their edges, following Kepler's Third Law, which was described in Chapter 8. This is called *differential rotation*. These disks are not stable, uniform mixtures of gas and dust, but are subject to specific kinds of instabilities when they are stimulated, such as by a collision with a smaller galaxy. As discovered by astronomers C.C. Lin and Frank Shu in the mid-1960s through a detailed analysis of the equations for such disks, they tend to form pairs of waves that sweep out through the disk in what are called *spiral density waves*. The benefit of this theory is that spiral arms will not be 'solid' arms of matter, which would tightly wind up at their centres due to differential rotation. Instead, spiral arms are merely gas density enhancements by about 20 to 30 per cent relative to the density of the underlying gas disk. These waves travel in a circular fashion around the nucleus of the galaxy, which contains the majority of the mass that stabilizes the disk. When this density wave passes over a molecular cloud, it can trigger cloud collapse, favouring the creation of massive stars. These stars produce enormous quantities of ionizing UV radiation, which then lights up the surrounding gas into various nebular forms. It is these massive stars in their nebulae that define the otherwise invisible spiral density wave. Also, the stars in the galaxy, which continue to orbit the nucleus of the galaxy, pass through these spiral density waves and receive a slight gravitational acceleration that changes their orbits. This can amplify the spiral density wave but only within a certain range of distances from the nucleus. Outside this distance, the effect is less efficient and the spiral density wave weakens. This makes the arms fade dramatically, defining the optical 'edge' to the galaxy.

This theory can be demonstrated by photographing a galaxy such as M-104 to enhance the Pop II stars, and comparing it to a second infrared photograph that emphasizes the young stars

and the disk of gas. It is easy to see from this that the spiral arms are embedded within the dominating halo of Pop II stars, and the density wave highlighted by OB stars and nebulae is a small effect.

A photograph of the M104 galaxy.

THE INTERSTELLAR MEDIUM

The interstellar medium of a spiral galaxy is generally very complex. Its discovery is credited to observations made in the early

1900s by Edward Barnard and Johannes Hartman, whose obser-vations of dark clouds and spectroscopic absorption lines led to the basic idea that interstellar space is filled with a gas and dust component that can form clouds. The advent of radio astronomy in the 1940s and 1950s led to the detection of interstellar clouds of hydrogen gas through its emission at a wavelength of 21 cm (8½ in). By the late 1960s and early 1970s, astronomers George Field, Christopher McKee and other astronomers had developed a three-component model for the interstellar medium consisting of cold molecular clouds, a warm inter-cloud medium rich in atomic hydrogen, and a hot component produced and heated by supernovae remnants.

Beginning in the mid-1970s, the molecular cloud component was intensively studied by radio astronomers. Dozens of different molecules were discovered in these dense, cold clouds. Their densities were upwards of 1000 molecules/cc at temperatures below 100 K. Infrared astronomers also detected very young, dust-enshrouded stars being formed in these clouds, which became known as the stellar nurseries of the Milky Way. Lower-density hydrogen clouds were also found throughout the plane of the Milky Way. Analysis of their motions helped to discern the spiral structure of the Milky Way. These dense clouds were typically found within 100 light years of the plane of the Milky Way.

The inter-cloud component is a dilute gas of hydrogen detected through its 21 cm (8½ in) radio emission line, and mapped extensively throughout the galaxy. At a density of about 0.5 atoms/cc and temperatures below 6,000 K they form a neutral but pervasive gas within 300 light years of the plane of the Milky Way. A second, much hotter inter-cloud component consists of ionized hydrogen at temperatures of 8,000 K and densities similar to the neutral component. The extent of this component is within 3,000 light years of the galactic plane.

The hot component has temperatures up to 10 million K and densities below 0.001 atoms/cc, although it is a fully ionized gas emitting via X-rays. This hot but dilute plasma occupies over

70 per cent of the volume of interstellar space and is heated by numerous supernova remnants whose hot plasmas expand and merge together over millions of years.

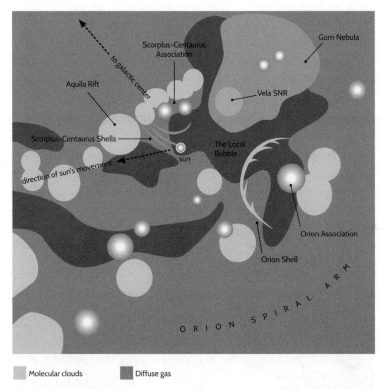

Molecular clouds   Diffuse gas

The solar system is located in the Local Bubble and close to the Local Fluff interstellar cloud. This diagram gives a sense of the local cloud population and the locations of some of the voids containing little interstellar gas.

The interactions between these three components leads to a very dynamic system of gas and clouds over time, which are in pressure equilibrium with each other and flow as a system under the gravitational influence of the stars that make up the dominant mass of the Milky Way itself. Detailed maps of these components near the Sun by astronomer Priscilla Frisch reveal that we live within a structure called the Local Bubble – a vast region of hot ISM created over 500,000 years ago when a nearby supernova exploded. Within this bubble are filamentary clouds. We are about to enter one of these – called the 'Local Fluff' – in the next 50,000 years.

OUR MILKY WAY

A combination of studies of globular clusters, open clusters, nebulae, pulsars and the interstellar medium can be combined into a roughly self-consistent model of the shape and structure of our Milky Way, as shown in this illustration created in 2017 by astronomer/artist Robert Hurt at CalTech. The total mass of the Milky Way has been determined in 2019 from Gaia satellite measurements of millions of stars and star clusters to be 1.5 trillion times the mass of our Sun within one million light years of the centre of the Milky Way. Only about 200 billion solar masses of this total is in the form of stars and interstellar gas clouds. The rest is in a form called Dark Matter, which will be discussed in a later chapter.

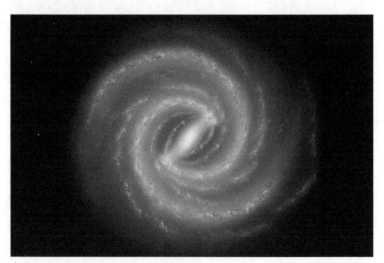

Artist's rendering of the major identified components of the Milky Way including major spiral arms and the bar-like shape of the nuclear region. Our Milky Way is classified as a barred-spiral galaxy based on the shape of the nucleus.

Key Points

- Galaxies are collections of billions of individual stars along with stray interstellar gas and dense clouds.

- Historically, galaxies are distinguished by their shapes as spirals, ellipticals or irregulars.

- The shape of a galaxy is a fossil record of the interactions it has had with other galaxies over its lifetime, primarily through a process of gravitational interaction and collision.

- The most dramatic galaxies are the spirals, whose arms are delineated by active, massive star formation episodes taking place in dense interstellar clouds.

- Among the oldest galaxies are the ellipticals, which may have formed within a few billion years after the Big Bang based on their abundance of older, element-poor stars.

Chapter 14

Interacting Galaxies

Galaxies are not fixed structures but alter shape over time as a result of both internal changes and interactions with the environment.

The most common form of interaction is the galaxy–galaxy collision in which two galaxies gravitationally interact with each other. At low speeds, this interaction can involve galaxy mergers and 'cannibalism', causing the larger of the two systems to absorb the interloper. This is also the favoured mechanism for growing larger galaxies from smaller dwarf galaxies. Astronomers think this has been the major galaxy-growing mechanism from the early history of the universe to the present time. At the typical relative speeds of nearby galaxies, about 300 km/s, galaxies can travel the average million-light year distances that separate themselves in about 1 billion years. This is enough time for many of these distant encounters to take place in the 12-billion-year history of a galaxy since the Big Bang (see pages 186–194). Dwarf galaxies, such as the Magellanic Clouds at a distance of 160,000 light years, are even now interacting with the Milky Way. They may still be around in the next 7 billion years, although gradually stripped of most of their stars.

When galaxies collide, the gravitational transformations can completely alter the individual galaxies and form an end state that is unlike that of the participating galaxies. In 4 billion years, the Milky Way and the Andromeda Galaxy, both large spirals, will collide and merge to produce a giant elliptical galaxy with a Hubble morphological class near E0, but with some gas and dust available to form a brief period of star formation. Other collisions can produce single spiral arm 'tidal tails' and other mixed shapes with complicated population mixtures.

This image shows the long ribbon of gas called the Magellanic Stream, which stretches nearly halfway around our Milky Way galaxy.

Our Milky Way has been steadily cannibalizing the smaller galaxies in its neighbourhood, and is currently disrupting the Large and Small Magellanic clouds, which are Pop I irregular galaxies. A flow of hydrogen gas called the Magellanic Stream shows that these dwarf galaxies have already had one encounter with the Milky Way and, by some calculations, will probably merge with the stellar population of the Milky Way within the next few billion years. Although these galaxies themselves will become invisible, their stars and some of their dense interstellar clouds will be discernible as having a high peculiar speed relative to other stars in the halo. Astronomers have also discovered several other families of 'high velocity stars' that no doubt indicate other dwarf galaxies that have long since been fully cannibalized. Recently, astronomer Stefan Meingast used the billion-star Gaia satellite survey to uncover 4,000 stars left over from a collision with the Milky Way and a globular star cluster perhaps a billion years ago.

There may be many of these 'star rivers' to be found as fossils of other encounters, hidden in plain sight among the stars of the Milky Way.

Our own Milky Way has been involved in multiple collisions with small dwarf galaxies in the past. In 2007, astronomers using the Spitzer Space Telescope identified three streams of stars connected to the nearby dwarf galaxies in Sagittarius and Canis Major, each containing 100 million stars. Currently, 12 streams have been identified as the remains of ancient dwarf galaxies. In 2012, astronomers detected a distortion in the distribution of stars above and below the plane of the Milky Way and attributed this to a collision with a very large dwarf galaxy about 100 million

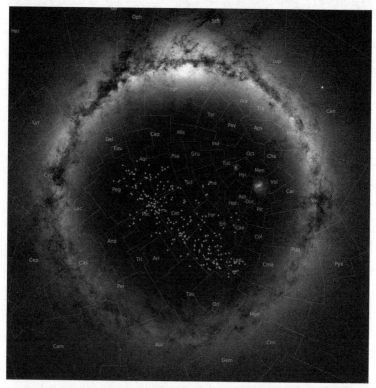

A nearby river of 4000 stars discovered by the billion-star Gaia Sky Survey in 2019.

years ago. The encounter may not have destroyed the dwarf galaxy, which may still be present within the 54 members of the Local Group today. In 2018, the Gaia satellite measured the properties of over 1.7 billion stars near the Sun, and verified the existence of at least one cloud of stars not rotating around the Milky Way like other stars, but instead on a peculiar trajectory through the galaxy. The cloud also contains stars with higher-than-normal abundances of heavy elements. This represents a collision that may have happened about 10 billion years ago and involved a metal-rich, very massive dwarf galaxy with a mass of 10 billion suns. It may even have been this collision that triggered the formation of the spiral arms in the Milky Way.

The most active regions of space for galaxy mergers and collisions is in the cores of dense clusters of galaxies, such as the Coma Cluster, or in very compact groups of galaxies such as Stephan's Quintet. These systems can have galaxy separations of no more than a few times the diameters of the galaxies themselves, and over millions of years this leads to frequent mergers.

In 4 billion years, the nearby Andromeda Galaxy and the Milky Way will collide. This is a single frame from a supercomputer-based simulation that shows this event as viewed from Earth.

High-speed encounters can be even more dramatic as the galaxies pass each other by at speeds beyond the gravitational capture speed. The result for galaxies of similar mass is the gravitational production of 'tidal arms' that can extend millions of light years. Across the nearby universe, we only see snapshots of such events at various stages. But modern supercomputer simulations, based upon Newton's Law of Gravity and tracing millions of 'mass points', yield striking movies of what some of these encounters can look like over the course of millions of years.

The details of the collision also affect the final outcome. For example, if the collision is exactly head-on so that the nucleus of one galaxy passes through the nucleus of another, beautiful ring galaxies can form like ripples on a pond. An expanding ring of star formation forms a near-perfect circle about the nuclear region.

The most dramatic effects of galaxy collisions are in the behaviour of the interstellar gas and dust clouds. These components of a galaxy have a far-greater extent than individual stars, and so collisions between them are frequent and intense. The likelihood that individual stars actually collide is extremely low due to their very small sizes compared to the vast interstellar spaces that separate them. For example, the pair of galaxies in Arp 299 located 134 million light years away shows a mash-up of cloud collisions triggering

Hoag's Object is a classical ring galaxy located in the constellation Serpens about 600 million light years from the Milky Way. It was probably created by a head-on collision between two galaxies, which caused a wave of star-forming activity to propagate away from the collision centre to form the ring.

the formation of massive stars, and a dramatically heated inter-stellar medium. This is detectable by the Chandra Observatory by its X-ray emissions. This galaxy is one of the most active star-forming galaxies in the local universe. Since 1990, eight supernovae have been detected in Arp 299.

The abundance of dust clouds forming massive luminous stars makes these collision and merger environments among the brightest infrared sources in the universe.

Another feature of a galaxy's environment that influences its evo-lution is the presence of gas between the gal-axies within a cluster. In Arp299, the produc-tion of some of this high-temperature me-dium is just beginning. However, the largest quantities are produced when spiral galaxies rich in interstellar material collide at high speed. The gas is far too hot to

The two merging galaxies in Arp 299 located in Ursa Major about 134 million light years away. Active star-forming events are taking place with new supernova detected from Earth every few years.

remain trapped by the galaxies, and so diffuses very quickly into the void between galaxies within a cluster. For some clusters, this medium is dense enough that as galaxies pass through it, it acts like a resisting medium and sweeps out the ISM housed within them. An example of this is ESO 137-001, which is falling into the Abell 3627 galaxy cluster.

These interactions were previously discovered in the 1960s and 1970s as elongated radio sources such as Perseus A, which seemed to be streamlined by their host galaxy's motion. Modern telescopes such as the Chandra X-ray Observatory can now directly image these stripped gases.

DARK MATTER

The most elusive material in the cosmos today is called Dark Matter. Originally discovered by astronomer Fritz Zwicky in 1933 within clusters of galaxies, and then in the 1970s by Vera Rubin in individual

The galaxy ESO 137-001 is shedding a 250,000 light year plume as it travels through the intracluster medium within this cluster of galaxies located 220 million light years away towards the constellation Triangulum.

galaxies, it is the gravitating substance that dominates the universe. It is five times more abundant than ordinary luminous matter: the stars, nebulae, ISM and other space material we can actually see. This has huge consequences for the way galaxies behave as they collide, as the majority of what is holding them together is an invisible, massive halo of dark matter in which the galaxy is embedded. Based on the motions of star clusters in its Halo region, our Milky Way has a mass of about 1.5 trillion suns out to 130,000 light years from its core, but only 10 per cent of this is in stars and the interstellar medium.

The Bullet Cluster (1E0657-558) is located 3.7 billion light years from the Milky Way, and is one of the classic examples of dark matter in clusters of galaxies. We see the two groups of galaxies embedded in their own dark matter halos (labeled A and B in the figure opposite) after a collision that took place about 150 million years ago. It left behind the hot intergalactic medium (the cloud located half way between A and B) seen emitting in X-rays. The dark matter follows the galaxies (it only interacts via

The Bullet Cluster showing two galaxy clusters (A and B) and colliding IGM clouds shown in between the clusters.

its gravity) and is completely unaffected by the collision, unlike the normal matter seen at the collision site.

Galaxy collisions can eject gas into the intra-cluster space of a galaxy cluster and can also eject stars. Although we cannot see the individual stars, we can detect their combined optical emission. Recently, astronomers Mireia Montes and Ignacio Trujillo at the University of New South Wales used Hubble Space Telescope images of six galaxy clusters to detect this faint light. Because these stars followed the gravitational wells created by dark matter and cluster galaxies, they were able to use this starlight to study the distribution of dark matter in these clusters to far higher resolution than previous methods allowed.

Key Points

- When galaxies collide, individual stars do not crash into each other, but the vastly larger interstellar medium and dense clouds do encounter each other.

- Galaxy collisions are powerful triggers of star-forming activity as interstellar clouds collide and portions of them are forced into collapse, leading to copious numbers of massive stars being formed.

- Galaxies found in clusters often encounter an intra-cluster medium created by previous galactic collisions. This very hot medium can dramatically affect the evolution of galaxies, and is often detected by its X-ray emission.

- Dark matter is a ubiquitous but invisible component to galaxies, but it can be detected by studying the collisions between clusters of galaxies and the motions of the galaxies and intra-cluster medium.

Chapter 15

Galactic Evolution

Soon after the Big Bang, dark matter provided a gravitationally lumpy stage into which normal matter, hydrogen and helium, eventually flowed. As this gas continued to cool, these vast supercluster-scale clouds fragmented into smaller cloudlets. Some of these cloudlets were the size of modern dwarf galaxies with masses of about 1 billion times the Sun's mass. As cooling

This artist's impression shows CR7, a very distant galaxy discovered using ESO's Very Large Telescope. It is by far the brightest galaxy yet found in the early universe and there is strong evidence that examples of the first generation of stars lurk within it.

continued, enormous populations of Pop III stars of 100 solar masses or more were able to gravitationally condense and explode within a few million years. This material, now enriched with some heavy elements, mingled with the existing gases to form the plenum out of which newer generations of stars could form. These became the Pop II stars we see today.

These Pop II stars formed within smaller dark matter gravity wells that became the halos for most modern-day galaxies. This process was so rapid that entire massive elliptical galaxies formed within a billion years after the Big Bang. Some of these formative events involved the cannibalism of smaller galaxies, in the same way that in 2 billion years our Milky Way and Andromeda galaxies will collide and merge to become a giant elliptical galaxy.

The infant galaxy EGS-zs8-1 is 13 billion light years distant and is phenomenally bright for its age. It has already achieved more than 15 per cent of the mass of our own Milky Way, but it had only 670 million years to do so since the Big Bang.

Some smaller dwarf galaxies, with masses of less than 1 billion suns, remained independent systems. They experienced multiple bursts of rapid star formation, leading to Pop I stars with nearly solar levels of elements, as early as 1 billion years after the Big Bang. The star formation rate

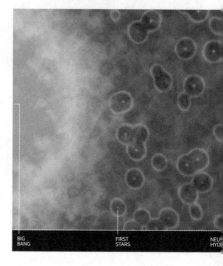

BIG
BANG

FIRST
STARS

NEU
HYD

in these galaxies was so rapid that they appear blue as they shine with intense ultraviolet light. Across the universe, these very numerous galaxies produced so much ultraviolet light that they reionized much of the cold, dark hydrogen gas in the intergalactic medium, marking the end of the dark ages and the beginning of a more transparent universe. This happened about 150 million to 1 billion years after the Big Bang. Not all the hydrogen gas became ionized at once. Numerous dark clouds lingered, some containing near-galaxy-sized masses. These clouds can be detected in the light of distant *quasars* as specific absorption lines seen in the spectra of hydrogen gas. Quasars are remote and highly energetic celestial objects, thought to contain massive black holes. Star formation in the dwarf galaxies contributed more than 50 per cent of the ionizing UV light because this light had an easier time escaping from these smaller collections of mass.

Galaxies did not form in isolation but were often in groups whose memberships changed through cannibalism. The speed

During the Reionization Era, massive ultraviolet stars converted the dark hydrogen clouds into a dilute ionized plasma, first through the emissions from individual Pop III stars (left), then through the combined star-forming activity in numerous dwarf galaxies (right).

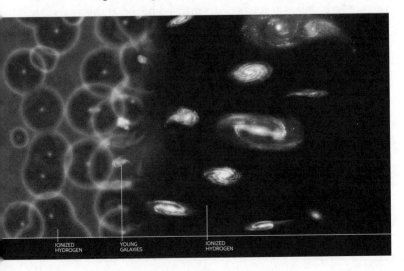

IONIZED HYDROGEN YOUNG GALAXIES IONIZED HYDROGEN

at which galaxies and clusters of galaxies formed is considered remarkable by astronomers. The farthest and youngest galaxy cluster identified today consists of four quasars found in a common cloud of hydrogen gas 1 million light years across located 10.6 billion light years from Earth. Its distance corresponds to a cosmic age of 3.2 billion years since the Big Bang. We only see the bright quasar cores of the host galaxies.

SUPERMASSIVE BLACK HOLES

Black holes can grow by absorbing material such as stars, ISM and even other black holes. In the dense cores of galaxies there are plenty of sources of infalling matter. Our Milky Way has a supermassive black hole containing over 4 million times our Sun's mass, which would imply a growth rate of about three solar masses every 10,000 years. This is dwarfed by the supermassive black hole at the core of the supergiant elliptical galaxy NGC 4889, which is 21 billion times the mass of our Sun at a distance of 308 million light years in the Coma Cluster. This would require a growth rate of 1.5 solar masses every year. Our Milky Way is barely considered an active galaxy based on the brightness and activity of its nuclear volume. However, NGC 4889 would be a quasar-level galaxy if it were currently being fed at this mass rate.

The favoured method for forming supermassive black holes rapidly is through mergers of galaxies. These black holes can grow to billions of solar masses by consuming local matter. But collisions allow black hole mergers that dramatically increase their growth rates. The most distant supermassive black holes, and therefore the youngest in cosmic age are the hyper-luminous quasar S50014+81 with 40 billion solar masses at 12.1 billion light years distance and TON 618 with 66 billion solar masses at 10.4 billion light years distance. These two supermassive black holes push the idea of growth-by-mergers to what are considered to be ridiculously high levels and possibly imply that a new mechanism must be considered. Nevertheless, the discovery of binary super-massive black holes in the merging galaxy 4C+37.11, each with a mass of about 15 billion suns at a distance of 750 million light years, continues to support this formation model. The quasar OJ 287 at a distance of 3.5 billion light years has a massive black hole with 18 billion solar masses being orbited every 12 years by a smaller black hole with a mass of about 100 million suns, so black hole mergers do occur at many cosmological epochs.

ACTIVE GALAXIES
Radio Galaxies

The detection of radio emissions from the Milky Way by Grote Reber in 1944 opened up a new window to the universe. Since then, many new and more sensitive 'radio telescopes' have been constructed. In addition to the radio emissions from the Milky Way, which could now be mapped in great detail, numerous 'radio stars' were also discovered. Many of these were not merely points of radio emissions in the sky, but could be resolved and mapped using radio 'interferometers' (see pages 14–15) in which two or more radio telescopes are combined across continents to detect detailed structure and form in celestial radio sources.

The Hercules A galaxy. Radio emission highlights the massive double jets. The visible light image shows the central host galaxy and other background galaxies.

One of the most powerful extra-galactic radio sources, Cygnus A (also called 3C 405), is a double radio source located some 600 million light years from the Milky Way in which the dumbbell-shaped pair of 'lobes' are separated by about 500,000 light years. Moreover, from photographic searches with the Mount Palomar 5 m (200 in) telescope, the centre of this radio source was found to coincide with a distorted pair of distant colliding galaxies.

In a growing number of cases, optical candidates could be found for these radio sources in which a single large radio source appeared offset from the optical object. In several cases, such as Virgo A (M-87), an optical 'jet' of light could be seen emanating from the galaxy's nucleus in the direction of one of the radio-emitting lobes. Not only that but over time and at high resolution, individual plasma clouds (called *plasmons*) many light years across could be seen travelling down the jet as though being ejected from some invisible source at the base of the jet, in the core of the host galaxy. The speeds of these plasmons have been measured to be large fractions of the speed of light, making them among the fastest physical phenomena seen in the universe.

Quasars

As optical searches of radio sources continued, one object called 3C48 was discovered in 1963 by astronomer Alan Sandage to have merely a faint star-like blue object at its centre. Astronomers Jesse Greenstein and Thomas Matthews were able to obtain a spectrum for this object and discovered that its lines made no apparent sense. The same year, Maarten Schmidt and Beverly Oke detected the optical counterpart to 3C273 and their spectroscopic work indicated a 'redshift' of z=0.16, which means a recession speed of 16 per cent that of the speed of light. It was Schmidt who correctly interpreted the wavelength shift as normal atomic lines displaced to longer wavelengths due to cosmic expansion. It was now possible to understand the earlier spectrum of 3C48; if the spectrum wavelengths were shifted to the red by about 37 per cent it implied a recession speed of nearly 110,000 km/sec. The term 'quasar' was coined by astronomer Hong-Yee Chiu in May 1964.

The hunt was now on for more quasars, leading to a catalogue of about 40 examples by 1968. Today, more than 200,000 quasars are known – most identified from the Sloan Digital Sky Survey. All observed quasar spectra have redshifts between $z=0.056$ and $z=7.085$. Applying Hubble's law and general relativity to these redshifts, it can be shown that they are between 600 million and 28 billion light years away (in terms of their actual cosmological distance). Because of the great distances to the farthest quasars and the finite velocity of light, they and their surrounding space appear as they existed in the very early history of the universe. The most distant known quasar, J1342+0928, is at a redshift of $z=7.54$ and existed when the universe was only 700 million years old. We are seeing the light from this object when the first stars and galaxies were forming in the universe.

By plotting the number of quasars at each redshift, astronomers have identified an Era of Quasar Formation that occurred between redshifts of $z=0.5$ and $z=3.0$, corresponding to a period about 2 to 5 billion years ago. Today, the formation mechanism for quasars appears to be less effective than it once was, so fewer examples exist in our part of the universe. In fact 3C273, with a redshift of $z=0.16$, remains the closest known quasar at a distance of 2.4 billion light years. Its luminosity amounts to over 4 trillion stars like our own Sun. Even so, it is not the most luminous quasar known. The quasar SDSS J0100+2802, discovered in 2015 at a redshift of $z=6.3$, produces 430 trillion times the light energy of our Sun, and we see its light when the universe was only 900 million years old.

In addition to quasars, and since the 1960s, a bewildering ensemble of peculiar galaxies have been discovered. Many show indications of activity in their dense nuclei. Studies of these 'active galaxies' at a variety of wavelengths from the radio and infrared to X-ray frequencies reveal three separate types of activity.

Starburst galaxies

These galaxies show indications of large numbers of massive stars being formed in a short span of time, and also evidence of many supernova events as some of these massive stars end their lives.

The starburst galaxy Henize 2-10 showing complex star formation and gas ejection.

Seyfert galaxies

These galaxies are powerful, compact sources of radio and infra-red radiation usually found in the cores of spiral-type galaxies. Their nuclei often contain ionized gas travelling at thousands of km/s as though expanding from some central source that has ejected these clouds.

The Circinus A seyfert galaxy showing bright nucleus and complex gas flows feeding a supermassive black hole at its centre.

BL Lacertids and Blazars

These objects are galaxies with bright star-like cores that vary in optical and radio brightness over the course of months or years. The first galaxy of this type was actually misidentified as an ordinary variable star in the Milky Way and designated BL Lacertae. Blazars are even more variable on timescales as short as hours, and also produce gamma-rays.

Studies of active galaxies have found that many are associated with colliding galaxies in which violent collisions between interstellar clouds provide the stimulus for forming numerous massive stars. For other active galaxies, such as the Seyferts and BL

Lacertids, it is thought that they represent a common process but viewed at different perspectives from Earth. These galaxies have massive black holes at their star-like cores, which are consuming matter from a surrounding accretion disk. Viewed edge-on you see a Seyfert-like phenomenon, but viewed face-on you are looking down the axis of a high-speed jet of plasma that changes its brightness rapidly to produce the 'BL Lac' and Blazar phenomena.

The BL Lacertid-type galaxy NGC 4380 with classic star-like nucleus.

Key Points

- The earliest stars that formed in the universe were made of pure hydrogen and helium and typically had masses greater than 100 suns. These Pop III stars supernovaed and spread enriched elements throughout the universe.

- Over time, galaxies formed massive central 'supermassive' black holes due to mergers and galactic cannibalism.

- The feeding of these supermassive black holes led to a variety of activity in galaxies including quasars, which were common in the universe but very rare today.

- The evolution of galaxies is driven by collisions with their neighbours that can lead to cannibalism and mergers, and also trigger the feeding of central supermassive black holes.

- It is believed that galaxies formed within the first 100 million years after the big bang, and grew steadily in size through mergers among smaller-massed objects.

PART VI

Cosmic
Structure

Chapter 16

Cosmic Structure

Galaxies are the building blocks of cosmic structure. Astronomer Sir William Herschel, working in the late 18th/early 19th century, using his 6m (20 ft) and 12m (40 ft) telescopes, glimpsed what this structure would look like. Before then galaxies, as we know them today, were merely indistinct smudges of light seen between the brighter foreground stars of the Milky Way. Herschel had already

William Herschel was a polymath musician, optician and astronomer who made substantial contributions to observational astronomy in the late 18th century.

discovered that some of the nebulae were 'full of stars'. He called them 'Island Universes'. By meticulously cataloguing their locations, he soon found hundreds of them clustering among the stars in the constellations Coma Berenices and Virgo. Herschel called these curious collections 'clouds'. It would not be until the first decades of the 20th century that their true distances and speeds were determined by means of spectroscopic and stellar studies. This was a tedious process involving measuring the Doppler speeds of each faint galaxy and assigning a distance to it based on a growing number of distance gauges, known as 'standard candles' (see page 202).

Galaxies often come in pairs or small groups, such as our own Milky Way with its two Magellanic Clouds, or the companion galaxies to the Andromeda Galaxy. Among the earliest renderings of close galaxy pairs was that of Lord Rosse, using his 'Great Telescope' at Birr Castle, Ireland, which first went into service in 1845.

Earliest drawing of the close pair of galaxies in Messier 51 by the Earl of Rosse.

A more dazzling compact group is Stephan's Quintet in the constellation Pegasus located 280 million light years away, discovered in 1877 by French astronomer Édouard Stephan.

Stephan's Quintet provides a rare opportunity to observe a galaxy group in the process of collision and merging into a single elliptical galaxy in the distant future.

At first, it was not known what to make of these pairings. Many might merely represent two galaxies along the same line of sight but not physically related to one another. It was not until the mid-1950s, when it became possible to calculate distances and velocities to galaxies, that it was clear that many of these systems were actually close to one another. Their shapes strongly hinted at profound gravitational interactions taking place between them. This led to the idea that some galaxy pairs and groups may actually be colliding systems of stars and gas.

By the early 1900s, it was already known that our own Milky Way was a member of a group of a dozen nearby galaxies including the Andromeda Galaxy as its other major member. Edwin Hubble, in his 1936 book *The Realm of the Nebulae*, referred to this collection as the 'Local Group'. Since that time, the Local Group has swelled to over 54 members. Most of these galaxies are of the dwarf variety – merely clusters of a few billion faint stars. A few are dramatic, and highly-

The Sagittarius Dwarf Irregular Galaxy is probably typical of the largest numbers of galaxies in the universe.

photogenic, spiral systems such as Andromeda (Messier 31) and Triangulum (Messier 33). The Sagittarius Dwarf Irregular Galaxy is at the farthest gravitational outskirts of the Local Group some 3.4 million light years from the Milky Way and is barely detectable photographically.

Edwin Hubble confirmed through observations at Lick Observatory that galaxies were beyond the Milky Way and were receding from the Milky Way at high speed as a result of cosmic expansion.

The question then arose, are groups and clusters of galaxies in the universe ubiquitous? Because of their substantial extent across the sky, a systematic search for more examples of galaxy groups and clusters had to await better photographic technology. Between 1949 and 1958, and under the guidance of Edwin Hubble, among others, the National Geographic Society commissioned the first all-sky photographic survey (POSS I) using the new 120 cm (48 in) Schmidt Telescope at Mount Palomar, in California. These photographs recorded images of billions of stars and galaxies and offered the data in a convenient format of pairs of 'red'- and 'blue'-filtered glass plates. This archive became the workhorse for generations of astronomers searching for the optical candidates for exotic radio and X-ray sources, as well as studies in galactic nebulae and extra-galactic structure.

George Abell was one of the first astronomers to systematically tackle the problem of the numbers and structures of galaxy clusters by using the POSS archive. His catalogue eventually identified over 4,000 galaxy clusters in the northern and southern hemispheres, and characterized them in terms of their richness and concentration.

Galaxy clusters vary enormously in their physical sizes as well as the numbers of members they contain. Our Local Group would barely make it into Abell's Richness Class 0. But clusters like the Coma Cluster or the Virgo Cluster discovered by Herschel in the 18th century tipped the limits of Richness Class 5 with well over 1000 galaxies each. The largest cluster known by 2018 is SPT-CLJ2106-5844, located 7.5 billion light years from the Milky Way, with a mass equal to 1.3×10^{15} suns. This would equal about 5,000 galaxies like our Milky Way, or easily ten times that number if most member galaxies are simple dwarfs, as for our Local Group.

Although the typical distances between member galaxies can be a million light years for less concentrated clusters, the most compact clusters may have average distances of only a few times the diameters of the member galaxies. At typical cluster speeds of 300 km/s, collisions between galaxies can be frequent over the multi-billion-year ages for these clusters. This leads to enormous changes to the space within the cluster. Low-speed collisions cause the galaxies to gently merge. But high-speed collisions can cause the gas, dust and clouds that make up the galactic interstellar medium (ISM) to be ejected from the galaxies and take up residence in the intra-cluster medium (ICM). This medium will be very hot due to the kinetic energy deposited into the gas as thermal energy. The gas, mostly hydrogen, may be so hot that it is ionized and is detected only through its X-ray emissions.

A consequence of a dense ICM is that other member galaxies passing through this material may themselves be dramatically affected. We can see this in the case of the galaxy ESO-137 located within the Abell 3627 cluster.

The preponderance of spindle-shaped 'lenticular' galaxies in some clusters may attest to the dramatic

George Abell discovered the clustering of galaxies and systematically catalogued the largest galaxy clusters within a few billion light years of the Local Group.

sweeping-out of a galaxy's ISM due to an ICM gas, leaving behind a dead galaxy with no new star-forming activity or dusty ISM.

SUPERCLUSTERS

When Abell plotted the locations of these catalogued clusters on a map of the entire sky, he was able to discern that they were not at all randomly distributed, but in many cases displayed higher-order clustering. Not only were galaxies found largely in clusters of varying size, but these clusters themselves combined with others across the sky to form clusters of clusters. By 1953, astronomer Gerard de Vaucouleurs had already discovered such large groupings in his study of our Local Group and its relationship with the Virgo Cluster. He found that galaxies within 200 million light years of the centre of the Virgo Cluster formed a flattened system he called the Local Supercluster.

In the 1960s and 70s, further investigations of Abell Clusters and the distribution of local galaxy clusters soon revealed a vast tapestry of superclusters, some far larger than our nearby Virgo Supercluster, and extending nearly 1 billion light years from the Milky Way. But what was so interesting about the distribution of these superclusters was that they were not randomly distributed across space as one might have expected from the assumptions of Big Bang cosmology. Instead, they were preferentially found along inconceivably vast filamentary structures encompassing still more mysterious empty regions called Voids. One of the largest of these, the Bootes Void, was discovered by Robert Kirchner in 1981 and is located about 700 million light years from the Milky Way. Spanning some 300 million light years, its interior is almost completely devoid of galaxies. Had the Milky Way been located at its centre, we would not have discovered the existence of other galaxies in the universe until the mid-1900s!

The investigation of superclusters, cosmic filaments and voids had to await newer observational techniques developed in the 1970s to massively increase the catalogue of galaxies for which Doppler shifts, or more accurately redshifts, could be determined.

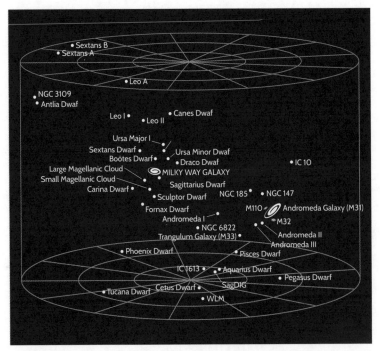

The Local Group includes our own Milky Way and the Andromeda Galaxy along with more than 50 other galaxies within 4 million light years of the Milky Way. The majority of these are classified as dwarf galaxies.

Because the local universe contained millions of galaxies, the older and time-consuming methods of one-at-a-time measuring had to be dramatically enhanced. The first astronomers to develop these techniques were Marc Davis, John Huchra and Margaret Geller at the Harvard-Smithsonian Center for Astrophysics (CfA), whose 'Z-Machine' could generate 30 redshifts every night. The CfA1 Redshift Survey, begun in 1977, catalogued over 2,000 galaxies. The follow-on CfA2 survey completed its work in the mid-1980s and added an additional 18,000 galaxies to the sample. These path-breaking surveys created nearly complete slices of the universe for bright galaxies, revealing not only the integrity and limits to many local superclusters, but delineating the scale of many voids as well.

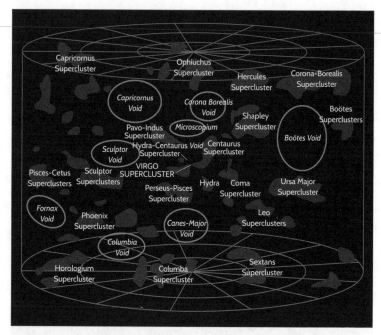

The local superclusters and voids constitute the dominant large-scale structures in the universe with galaxies and galaxy groups found within filamentary concentrations surrounding voids in which few galaxies exist.

Additional, even larger, surveys of fainter galaxies were completed during the heyday of redshift research in the 1990s and 2000, with even more efficient technologies becoming available including large-format digital cameras and fibre-optic, multi-channel spectrometers capable of calculating one thousand redshifts at a time. For example, the Sloan Digital Sky Survey (SDSS) Main Galaxy Sample, completed in 2002, determined redshifts for over 100,000 galaxies across one-sixth of the sky. Subsequent SDSS surveys will increase this to over one million galaxies.

What has emerged from this cartography of the universe during the last half of the 20th century is that galaxies are prefer-entially found within superclusters, which themselves form cos-mic filaments surrounding a complex and even foam-like patina of voids. The origin of this structure is deeply embedded in events taking place near the Big Bang itself.

The cataloguing of millions of galaxy redshifts allowed astronomers to investigate the motions of galaxies and their complex gravitational interactions spanning millions of light years of intergalactic space. Galaxies, in essence, became test particles that traced out gravitational flows of cosmic matter. This effort, enhanced by powerful supercomputer calculations based on Newtonian gravity and general relativity, led to the mapping of the local cosmic velocity field.

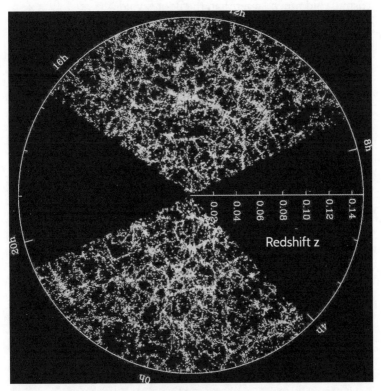

A comparison of the CfA and Sloan Redshift Surveys which shows that individual galaxies are generally located along filamentary concentrations of clusters and superclusters spanning the local universe.

Since the 1980s, astronomers have known that the Local Group is falling into the Virgo Supercluster and that this entire ensemble of thousands of galaxies is in turn moving towards a distant concentration of matter called the Great Attractor. Behind it and much farther away is another huge concentration of galaxies called the Shapley Supercluster. In addition to these flows of matter, there is also a region of reduced mass discovered in 2017 by astronomer Yehuda Hoffman called the Dipole Repeller, because galaxy motions seem to be emanating from this region of space. In fact, because gravity is only attractive, this means that the 'Repeller' region is actually a volume of space containing very little matter – a huge cosmic void much larger than the Bootes Void.

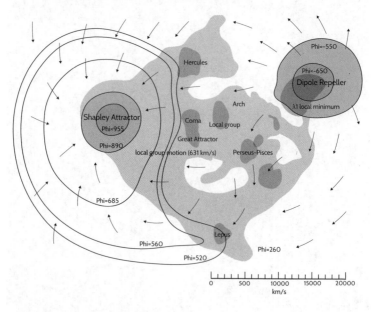

Data from thousands of local galaxies reveal a net doppler movement in the direction of the Shapley Supercluster.

Key Points

- Galaxies are collections of billions of stars and form the most elementary basis for structure in the universe.

- Galaxies often appear in pairs, groups and clusters which can have thousands of member galaxies. Our Milky Way is a member of the Local Group of galaxies.

- Clusters of galaxies often appear in larger groups called superclusters consisting of dozens or hundreds of separate clusters of galaxies.

- Clusters and superclusters form filamentary shapes spanning hundreds of millions of light years and surrounding vast voids in space where few galaxies are found.

- The large-scale structure of the cosmos is determined by the distribution of dark matter which accounts for most of the gravitating material in the universe.

Chapter 17

The Big Bang

Modern cosmology dates from the publication of Sir Isaac Newton's *Principia* (1687–1726), in which he used his Universal Law of Gravitation to propose the universe must be infinite and filled with a homogeneous distribution of matter, presumably stars and 'extragalactic nebulae'. He surmised that, were this not the case, the gravitational forces would not balance out exactly, and the universe would be in a state of gravitational collapse. It was an initial first guess that soon caused problems.

When you look into the night sky you notice the stars and the darkness of space between the stars. According to Thomas Diggs in the 17th century, later attributed to Heinrich Olbers in 1823, if the universe were infinite and uniformly filled with stars, the sky should be blindingly light. In an infinite universe, every line of sight should encounter the surface of a distant star. The *inverse-square law* (see pages 37–8) for light diminution would

Albert Einstein developed the theory of General Relativity from which all of modern 'Big Bang' cosmology has been developed.

reduce its intensity, but at each distance in a uniform cosmos, the number of stars increases as the square of the distance. The result is that each distance contributes a constant amount to the brightness of the sky, and in the sum of a vast cosmos, the sky should have the brightness and temperature of the surface of a single star.

The resolution of Olbers Paradox, as it came to be known, was overtaken in the early 1900s by the development of Albert Einstein's Theory of General Relativity. From this theory, a new generation of cosmological theories was developed and observationally tested.

In 1915, Einstein offered a cosmological model for a static universe, which he thought was the prevailing view at the time. To compensate for gravity otherwise causing the collapse of the universe, he added a *cosmological constant*. This acted as an antigravity force to balance gravity and cause the universe to be fixed in time and space. In the early-1920s, other physicists such as Georges Lemaître, Willem de Sitter and Alexander Friedmann used Einstein's cosmological equations to develop the foundations for modern cosmology.

Einstein and de Sitter investigated nearly empty universes where the cosmological constant was present and found that these should expand in an exponential manner. It was soon discovered that the original reason for adding a cosmological constant was implausible. The constant would have to be tuned exactly, and any natural deviation from this mathematically exact value would cause the universe to expand or contract.

Alexander Friedmann and Georges Lemaître, meanwhile, identified solutions to the equations in which, without a cosmological constant, the universe would manifest three distinct types. The distinction between these types depended on how the average density of the universe compared to the critical density – the ratio of these two was identified by the Greek letter omega (Ω). If the density were greater than critical ($\Omega > 1$) the geometric shape of space would be that of the surface of a sphere. That meant that the universe would expand to a maximum size and then collapse. If the density were equal to critical ($\Omega=1$) the universe would expand indefinitely, reaching an infinite size but with a geometry for space that would be Euclidean and flat. If the density were less than critical ($\Omega < 1$) the universe would reach an infinite size but its geometry would have a negative curvature, like the surface of a saddle. This connection between the measurable average density of the universe and its global geometry and evolution was a dramatic and defining moment for observational cosmology. There was now a specific methodology one could take as an astronomer to decide what type of universe we inhabited that was both physically and mathematically rigorous in logic. But there was also another prediction from these Friedmann Cosmologies that could be put to the test, and this was discovered by Georges Lemaître.

The Friedmann equations described the cosmic expansion in terms of the change in the scale of the cosmos. Galaxies were located at fixed geometric points but their physical separations were controlled by a 'scale factor' that changed over cosmic time. The galaxies themselves did not move through space by changing their co-ordinates, as happens in normal space when we travel from New York City to Paris. Instead the scale of space dilated as the universe evolved. What Lemaître discovered was that this scale change in time would be reflected in the apparent speeds of galaxies receding from us as the universe expanded. The relationship would be very simple: of the mathematical form $V=Hd$, where V is the recession speed and d is the distance to the galaxy. H is what we now the Hubble Constant and is a ratio

Alexander Friedmann used Einstein's general relativity to find families of solutions for the evolution of the universe, which included the 'Big Bang' models.

between recession speed and distance that reflects the scale factor change in time, and which has the units of 1/time.

Within a few years, astronomer Edwin Hubble independently discovered from his studies of the speeds and distances of near-by galaxies that these were related in a linear fashion, now called Hubble's Law. When Hubble's Law was related back to the Friedmann equations, not only did it confirm an expanding universe but the Hubble Constant could be directly related to the critical density of matter needed to decide between the various cosmic models. Since the 1930s, the main effort in cosmology has been to determine the Hubble Constant precisely and to inventory all of the forms of gravitating 'stuff' in the universe that contributes to its average density. From this, the value for H could be exactly determined. On the way to pinning down the exact value for H, further details of an expanding cosmos were discovered.

THE HOT BIG BANG

In the 1930s, Lemaître proposed that the universe began as a hot, dense 'atom' that exploded. By the 1940s, physicists George Gamow and Ralph Alpher worked out the nuclear physics of such a hot dense system and made several seminal discoveries. First, because of the pace of expansion and the falling temperature, you would only be able to synthesize from the plasma of neutrons, protons and electrons the elements hydrogen and helium. Secondly, the incessant collisions would create an intense field of million-degree gamma-ray light. As the universe expanded and cooled, this would currently have a temperature of about 20 K. It became known as the cosmic background radiation (CBR). Astronomers worked to test this idea against competing theories, such as Fred Hoyle's 'Steady State Universe' of the 1950s. In fact, Hoyle in a radio interview dismissed the Lemaître cosmology as the 'Big Bang' theory – a moniker that has remained to this day. Steady State cosmology could not explain the existence of a handful of 'primordial' elements, nor the background radiation, which should be a *black-body spectrum* in intensity with a definite temperature near 20 K. A black-body spectrum shows how much energy a body is emitting across all electromagnetic wavelengths, and it has a unique shape if the object is in complete thermal equilibrium with the radiation it emits. The wavelength at the peak of the emission can be related directly to the temperature of the object by using Wein's Law which says that wavelength × temperature = constant. For a temperature of 20 kelvins, the peak wavelength will be at 145 micrometers. As it would turn out, the actual temperature was found to be 2.7 K, so the peak of the emission across the sky should be found at a wavelength of 1.1 millimetres. Because the initial gamma ray emission of the CBR has been redshifted by cosmic expansion to longer microwave lengths, it is called the Cosmic Microwave Background Radiation or CMBR.

The initial discovery of the CMBR was made quite by accident by the radio astronomers Arno Penzias and Robert Wilson in 1964, who were mapping the radio emission from the Milky Way and trying to reduce the noise in the detected signals. The effort since then has been to map this CMBR across the sky and more precisely determine its spectrum shape and temperature. This background radiation had previously been discovered in 1941 by Andrew McKellar, who was studying the cyanogen (CN) molecule in interstellar space. He discovered that the strength of its spectral lines could only be understood if there was some kind of interstellar radiation field with a temperature of 2.3 K. He did not connect this finding with any cosmological explanation, however.

Fred Hoyle proposed a significant alternative to 'Big Bang' cosmology called Steady State Theory, which was ultimately found to be incompatible with the discovery of the Cosmic Microwave Background Radiation.

THE COSMIC MICROWAVE BACKGROUND RADIATION

The 1960s and 70s were an exciting time for measuring as accurately as possible the spectrum and temperature of the CMBR using rockets, balloons and many other technologies. The definitive measurement of its spectrum and temperature was provided by NASA's Cosmic Background Explorer (COBE) satellite, launched in 1989. Its Far Infrared Spectrometer (FIRAS) instrument developed by John Mather measured its precise properties by a simultaneous comparison with a reference black body on the satellite. The result was a perfect black body spectrum with a temperature of 2.725 K.

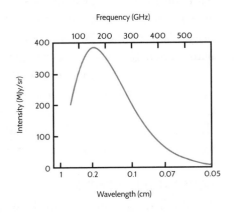

The COBE satellite also carried the Differential Microwave Radiometer (DMR) developed by George Smoot. This instrument compared the brightness of the CMBR from two sky locations 60° apart at three frequencies. The contribution to the radio noise issuing from the Milky Way was subtracted to produce an all-sky map of intensity variations.

Spectrum of the CMBR from the COBE FIRAS instrument which proved that it had a shape consistent with black-body emission at a single temperature, and conclusively confirmed the Hot Big Bang theory in 1990.

The result was that the CMBR was very smooth across the sky to 1 part in 10, but at 1 part in 100,000 there was a patina of irregularities in brightness that could be traced to slight temperature variations when the universe was only 380,000 years old. Further improvements in the resolution of these irregularities was obtained by the NASA Wilkinson Microwave Anisotropy Probe (WMAP) and the ESA Planck Satellites in the 1990s, which not only confirmed the COBE results but showed even smaller variations.

The CMBR that we see today was last in contact with matter about 380,000 years after the Big Bang. At that time, the plasma of the universe consisting of the nuclei of the primordial elements, electrons and the photons of the CBR were still interacting with each other. After that time, the temperature of the cosmos dropped below about 3,000 K and the free electrons combined with the nuclei to form the first neutral atoms. This rapidly evolving neutral primordial gas replaced the high-temperature plasma and so the CBR photons no longer interacted strongly with matter. The universe, essentially, became transparent to the CBR light. The variations we see in the CMBR today are the traces of how lumpy the matter in the cosmos was around this epoch, which occurred about 380,000 years after the Big Bang. In a later chapter, we will see how these variations provide fossil evidence for still earlier events in cosmic history.

PRIMORDIAL ELEMENTS

The detailed calculations of nucleosynthesis as the Big Bang proceeded points to a time about 20 minutes after the Big Bang when the available neutrons and protons could no longer interact to produce elements heavier than beryllium (3 protons, 4 neutrons). Thermonuclear fusion can only proceed if protons and neutrons can be forced together so that they are closer than about 10^{-14} cm. At this separation, the strong nuclear force can overcome the electromagnetic charge-repulsion force between protons to bind them together. This requires fast-moving and therefore 'hot' plasmas of neutrons and protons. The plasma also has to be dense enough that copious amounts of the fusion products are left over. At the start of the so-called Nucleosynthesis Era, about three minutes after the Big Bang, deuterium (1 proton, 1 neutron) was now available in large enough quantities for it to form the basis for the production of heavier elements such as helium (2 protons, 2 neutrons). By about 10 minutes, all the free neutrons began to decay and vanish from the plasma, and the production of elements such as lithium and beryllium could begin. But the universe by 20 minutes after the Big

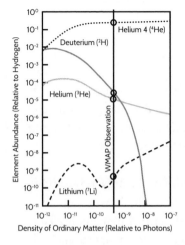

The result of Big Bang nucleosynthesis after 10,000 seconds. The curves show the expected abundances of the primordial elements given the number of CMB photons, along with the measurements by the WMAP satellite.

Bang had cooled to 300 million K, and this was too cool for element building to continue. By 20 minutes after the Big Bang, cosmic matter consisted of 75 per cent hydrogen and 25 per cent helium, with vanishingly small traces of deuterium, lithium and beryllium.

Astronomers have determined the cosmic abundances of the primordial elements in a variety of diverse sources such as the atmosphere of old stars, and planets like Jupiter. There are no instances for which the helium abundances are below 23 per cent that are consistent with a cosmological origin, since there are no mechanisms that destroy helium nuclei in the cold atmospheres of stars.

The predictions made by Big Bang cosmology for primordial element abundances, along with the details of the CBR and CMBR, are considered the major successes of Big Bang cosmology that have not been accounted for by any other contender for describing the universe as we see it today. Nevertheless, these features, along with the details of cosmic expansion, continue to be heavily investigated to make Big Bang cosmology a high-precision theory.

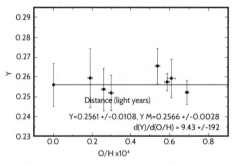

Helium abundances (Yp) for a variety of very old stars, which indicates a primordial abundance for helium of 25 per cent.

Key Points

- The origin and evolution of the universe is accurately described by Big Bang cosmology developed in the 1920s and is based upon Einstein's theory of general relativity.

- The predicted expansion of the universe from Big Bang theory was discovered by Edwin Hubble in the late 1920s and is described by Hubble's Law: $V = Hd$ where v is the recession speed and d is the galaxy distance. H is a constant known to be about 70 km/sec/megaparsec.

- A second prediction from Big Bang cosmology is the existence of the Cosmic Microwave Background Radiation (CMBR) discovered in the early 1960s and precisely measured by NASA's COBE satellite in 1990.

- The CMBR implies the universe began as a dense and very hot mass of plasma.

- The origin of the primordial elements hydrogen and helium arose from the first ten minutes after the Big Bang. Other elements were created by stellar supernova at a later cosmic time.

Chapter 18

The Dark Universe

Until the discovery of extra-galactic nebulae, the essential ingredients to the universe were considered to be the luminous stars. The distances to many of the nearby galaxies were determined by Edwin Hubble in the late 1920s. For cosmological discussions, these were the farthest outposts of luminous matter in the universe, spreading out to the limits of telescopic sight.

The discovery of the interstellar medium (ISM) during the first-half of the 20th century, first by optical means and then by its radio emissions, showed there was more cosmic matter than the stellar galaxies alone. Through its radio emission at the 21 cm (8½ in) wavelength of the 'hydrogen line', the ISM was carefully mapped throughout the Milky Way and other nearby galaxies, but the amount found therein was seldom more than 10 per cent of the total mass of the host galaxy as measured by their stellar content. This cold ISM, however, was also a companion to a hot ISM of ionized hydrogen and other common elements that could not be seen via the neutral atomic hydrogen emission. X-ray telescopes would detect this emission as a diffuse glow permeating some sectors of the Milky Way where supernova remnants had recently blasted their way through the neutral ISM and ionized it. Nevertheless, estimates of the total mass that could reside in this ISM was also a small percentage of the total galactic mass.

Image of the core of the Coma Cluster revealing hundreds of individual galaxies clustered together within a volume of space only 10 million light years across.

In 1933, CalTech astronomer Fritz Zwicky made the startling announcement that the Coma cluster of galaxies was hiding a considerable amount of mass, far beyond the small contributions of interstellar gases. Not only did Coma have this 'missing mass' problem, but several other clusters of galaxies had the same deficit.

This startling finding came about when Zwicky determined the velocities for eight galaxies in the Coma cluster whose actual membership includes over 1,000 galaxies. He discovered that the range of speeds for the galaxies in the Coma galaxies was ±360 km/s. This implied a mass for the cluster, assuming these eight galaxies were typical, that would be over 50 times more than the mass one would determine from the luminous matter in the galaxies themselves. According to Zwicky, '*If this* [overdensity] *is confirmed we would arrive at the astonishing conclusion that dark matter is present* [in Coma] *with a much greater density than luminous matter.*' Three years later, Sinclair Smith discovered the same effect in his study of 32 members of the Virgo cluster.

On the galactic scale, investigations of the nearby Andromeda Galaxy by Horace Babcock in 1939, subsequent studies by Vera Rubin and Kent Ford in 1970, and radio astronomers Morton Roberts and Robert Whitehurst in 1975, found that the outer regions of this spiral galaxy beyond the bright stellar disk also revealed a 'dark matter' problem. By measuring the rotation speed of a spiral galaxy at various distances from its luminous core, this 'rotation curve' should have a very distinct shape once you reach the limits

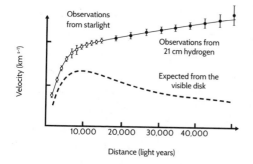

Rotation curve of Messier 33 showing that the speed of the stars and interstellar gas (top curve) exceeds the speeds predicted if all the mass were located within the visible galaxy (bottom dashed curve).

to the galaxy's stellar disk. The relationship is given by Kepler's Third Law, and is illustrated by the dashed line in the diagram (left) on Messier-33.

What the rotation curve actually represents is a way to measure the total mass of a galaxy inside the selected radius. If all the mass is largely confined to the bright nuclear region, the curve should reach a maximum, and then the speeds should decline from that point outwards. This was not found for the Andromeda Galaxy and a number of other carefully studied systems. To account for these flattened curves, the galaxy must contain large quantities of dark matter far greater than the mass found in the luminous stars. Our own Milky Way also shows evidence for dark matter.

Vera Rubin was an astrophysicist at the Carnegie Institute in Washington DC where she worked on investigating the rotation curves of galaxies, wishing to avoid in the late 1960s the controversial topics of Milky Way structure and quasars while working with astronomers Margaret and Geoffry Burbidge. Her investigations of 'normal' galaxy rotation turned up anomalies that led her to the discovery of dark matter in individual galaxies, which dramatically improved the detection and characterization of this hidden, gravitating component to the universe.

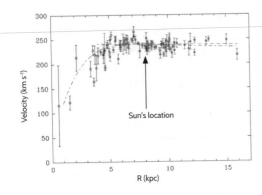

The Milky Way rotation curve shows that, like many galaxies, the flatness of the curve beyond the orbit of the sun requires a significant amount of invisible dark matter to account for the high speeds.

The origin of this dark matter has been a matter of intense speculation since the 1960s. Candidates have included neutrinos with large masses, dim dwarf stars, black holes and even large numbers of planetary-sized objects. The problem has been that the dark matter mass distribution suggests that the average density of dark matter in the Milky Way is about 10 times that of stellar sources, so we should see plenty of evidence for this material among the stars in the solar neighbourhood. No such dark material or objects have yet been found.

An artist's rendering of the Milky Way dark matter halo based upon a variety of techniques for measuring the speeds of nearby galaxies and their gravitational accelerations towards the Milky Way.

At the present time, the best model for dark matter in the Milky Way involves studying the detailed speeds and distances of nearby galaxies and the Magellanic Clouds. From this, the Milky Way can almost literally be 'weighed'. The result is that about 95 per cent of the galaxy is composed of dark matter. The luminous matter makes up approximately 3×10^{11} solar masses. Recent observations by the Gaia satellite of the motions of globular clusters along with Hubble Space Telescope observations leads to a total gravitational mass for the Milky Way of 1.5 trillion solar masses out to a distance of about 130,000 light years. Most of this mass is dark matter within an extended halo, and within which the 160 globular star clusters and stars in our Milky Way exist as a flattened, spiral disk.

COSMOLOGICAL DARK MATTER

The discovery of large quantities of dark matter in the halos of individual galaxies and in clusters of galaxies had immediate cosmological consequences. The maps of the minute fluctuations in the CMBR provided by the NASA COBE mission suggested a weakly clumpy universe by about 360,000 years after the Big Bang, but when these irregularities were evolved forward in time to the present era using only the gravity of the known luminous matter, the clustering was too weak to account for what is seen today. This led to, or was contemporaneous with, various mathematical experiments to account for the clustering today by adding-in hot dark matter (HDM) and cold dark matter (CDM). The former would be in the form of a very hot gas that would not be directly detectable, the latter would be a colder form of material. Generally, the current structure could not be accounted for unless the missing mass found in galaxies and clusters of galaxies was cosmological in extent. In addition, if this added material were in the form of *baryons* (sub-atomic particles such as protons and neutrons), it would upset the calculations of the abundances of the primordial elements. Physicists called this material, proposed in the 1970s, weakly interacting massive particles (WIMPS). Other forms of dark matter based upon dark stars, black holes and other dense dark forms of baryons were called massive compact halo objects (MACHOS). However, the addition of these baryons would also upset the observed ratios of the abundances of primordial elements.

The NASA WMAP spacecraft used a sophisticated version of the COBE DMR instrument to map the CMBR at high resolution, and made high-precision measurements of dark matter and dark energy.

The NASA WMAP spacecraft launched in 2001 was instrumental in providing a refined and high-resolution (0.2°) look at the CMBR, and from this new data, a precise inventory of the gravitating material in the cosmos was first obtained. When the data was analysed through the cosmology of a Friedmann universe with a cosmological constant, Λ, and CDM, the final high-precision values for our Λ-CDM universe were obtained.

- Our universe is 13.77 billion years old.
- The geometry is within 0.4 per cent of being as flat as Euclidean space.
- Baryonic matter accounts for 4.6 per cent of the gravitating material in the universe.
- Non-baryonic 'matter' accounts for 24 per cent of the gravitating material in the universe.
- There is a 'dark energy' (Λ) component amounting to 71.4 per cent of the material in the universe.

With this new high-precision data, and a confirmation of the accuracy of the Λ-CDM cosmological model, it was now possible to run detailed supercomputer simulations to explore how this dark matter and energy affected the way that baryonic matter clumped and clustered as the universe aged to the present time.

Preliminary supercomputer simulations were begun in the 1970s with programs that followed thousands of mass points in an evolving universe. By 1990, this number had jumped to simulations involving one million 'galaxies'. By 2000 over 100 million

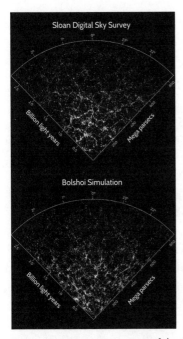

Supercomputers are now powerful enough to simulate the growth of clustering in the evolving universe. The 2012 Bolshoi simulation with dark matter included matches almost exactly the observed statistical clustering of galaxies seen in the Sloan survey of one million galaxies.

galaxies were simulated in such massive supercomputer efforts as the Millennium Simulation Project in 2005, and the Bolshoi Simulation in 2012. Most recently, in 2018, the Illustris Next Generation simulation at the High-Performance Computing Center Stuttgart, Germany has followed the formation from 30 billion cosmic gas elements as they form one million galaxies in a volume of space one billion light years across. The simulation takes two months and generates over 500 terabytes of data. From this simulation, the exact behaviour of dark matter interacting with normal matter can be followed through the formation of large cosmic structures and the halos of individual galaxies. Even the formation of supermassive black holes and their effect on surrounding galactic matter can be followed.

On the galactic scale, it is now possible to use clusters of galaxies and gravitational lensing (see page 24) to map out

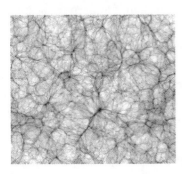

Simulation of a 1.2 billion light year region of baryonic matter forming cosmic structure with dark matter included.

where the dark matter is located in a number of clusters. The most famous of these is the Bullet Cluster. When these two clusters of galaxies collided, the dark matter was not affected and moved with the galaxies, but the gas (baryons) was left behind and formed shock-heated plasma. This demonstrates that dark matter only interacts through its gravity and cannot be detected by electromagnetic means (light, radio, X-rays). In this instance, it was detected by its gravitational lensing of background galaxy images.

COSMOLOGICAL DARK ENERGY

Among the other findings by the WMAP study of the CMBR was that a significant amount of 'dark energy' also coexisted with the dark matter and baryons in our universe. This dark energy behaved like the cosmological constant introduced in the early 20th century by Albert Einstein and Willem de Sitter and is historically represented by the Greek letter Λ. The implication of a non-zero Λ was staggering but not entirely unanticipated.

For decades it had been automatically included in modern Big Bang cosmological models because it was deemed another factor in the theory that had to be proven to not exist through the uses of observational data. Generally, its magnitude was considered unmeasurable by most studies. In 1998, the first true signs of this cosmological factor were discovered by two teams of researchers who used Type 1a supernovae as 'standard candles': the Supernova Cosmology Project led by Saul Perlmutter at the Lawrence Berkeley Laboratory, and the High-Z Supernova Search Team led by Adam Reiss from Johns Hopkins University. These supernovae, produced when a white dwarf orbiting a star explodes, should theoretically all have about the same peak luminosity because the white dwarf stars have about the same masses (1.44 solar masses). When a distant supernova is identified as a Type 1a supernova, its apparent brightness can be related to its true peak brightness, and a cosmological distance determined. When this was done for several dozen supernova, they were found to be much farther away than their cosmological distance implied. A number of explanations were tried for this effect, including dust near the supernovae and white dwarf masses not being exactly the same, but none could easily explain this effect. The simplest explanation became that our universe in recent time has started to accelerate in its expansion.

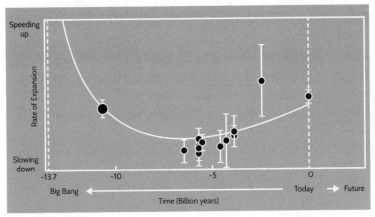

The accelerated expansion of the universe from supernova data reveals that about 9 billion years ago dark energy began to overtake the normal expansion rate predicted by standard Big Bang cosmology without a 'cosmological constant'.

THE ORIGINS OF DARK MATTER AND DARK ENERGY

Currently there are candidates for dark matter including a new family of particles called neutralinos predicted by some versions of supersymmetry theory – the next step beyond the Standard Model. Intense experimental work has been in progress for over a decade to detect these particles, but to no avail by 2019. As for dark energy, its behaviour is similar to what would be expected for a new quantum field in nature, possibly related to the Higgs boson or the hypothetical Inflaton boson, which triggered the inflation of the universe (see page 214). Just as for dark matter, there are no candidates for this new field of nature that have been experimentally identified.

Key Points

- Early studies of how galaxies rotate by Vera Rubin suggested that large amounts of 'dark matter' must be present, but not in the form of stars or interstellar gas.

- Studies of clusters of galaxies by Fritz Zwicky discovered that galaxies are moving far too fast within these clusters for them to be gravitationally bound, and so dark matter was needed on vast scales to stabilize them.

- Observations of the Cosmic Microwave Background Radiation by the COBE and WMAP spacecraft established that 4.6 per cent of the universe is ordinary matter but that 24 per cent is in the form of dark matter.

- Dark matter dominates the structure of the universe on its largest scales and defines the filamentary shapes of the clustering of galaxies on scales of 100 million light years or larger.

- Dark energy accounts for 71.4 per cent of the cosmos and is responsible for the accelerated expansion of the universe. Its origin is currently unknown.

Chapter 19

Early Cosmic History

In Chapter 17, we explored the Hot Big Bang theory from the era of the cosmic background radiation at 380,000 years after the Big Bang (let's abbreviate this to ABB) back to the start of the Nucleosynthesis Era at about three minutes after the Big Bang. In fact the entire history, structure and contents of the universe from the present day to a time three minutes after the Big Bang can be investigated using the tools, techniques and theories of astrophysics. But to explore the state of the universe prior to this time, we have to dramatically broaden the scope of astrophysical investigation to include high-energy particle physics, theories about the nature of space, time and matter, and such tools as accelerators and supercomputers. The term 'astrophysics' as an amalgam of 'astronomy' and 'physics' still represents the study of the contents and evolution of the universe by applying our knowledge of physics, but the tools and knowledge base have been greatly expanded.

We studied the astrophysics of gamma-ray sources in the sky with detectors (telescopes) that resembled those used in the study of nuclear physics. Astrophysics applied to the universe must now incorporate a steady stream of information gleaned from particle accelerators as our new 'telescopes' for studying the events taking place during early cosmic history. We no longer speak about stars, planets and galaxies as the basic currency of the universe, but we speak in terms of the elementary particles and forces through which they interact.

To delve into still earlier times, we need to use a significant prediction from Big Bang theory in which the temperature of the cosmic background radiation (and matter) can be related to specific moments in time. That relationship is:

$$T = \frac{10^{10}}{\sqrt{t}}$$

where t is the time in seconds (s) after the Big Bang (ABB) and T is the temperature in kelvins (K). For example, at the start of the Nucleosynthesis Era, at $t = 200$ s, we find that $T = 700$ million K. Another useful equation relates the energy carried by individual CBR photons to the current time:

$$E = \frac{0.00086}{\sqrt{t}}$$

so that at the start of the Nucleosynthesis Era, E = 61,000 electron-Volts (eV), a popular energy unit in nuclear physics (equivalent to 0.00006 GeV). On the eV scale, a gamma-ray photon with an energy of 1 million eV (1 MeV) can fission an atomic nucleus, but a photon with 1 eV is barely able to ionize a typical atom.

The description of early cosmic history before the Nucleosynthesis Era is largely a description of high-energy phenomena that have been investigated in detail by physicists during much of the 20th century through to the present time. This research is accomplished by using large particle accelerators, which collide elementary particles and generate new forms of matter. The cataloguing of these elementary particles and their forces and the mathematical theory that describes their properties and interactions, makes up the entirety of what is called the Standard Model.

The Standard Model consists of six particles called leptons and six particles called quarks. Among the leptons are the familiar electrons and neutrinos. The quarks, meanwhile, combine in twos and threes to make up the protons, neutrons and other common 'heavy' particles, also called *baryons*. Only the proton is a truly stable baryon. A free neutron will decay in about 600 seconds into a

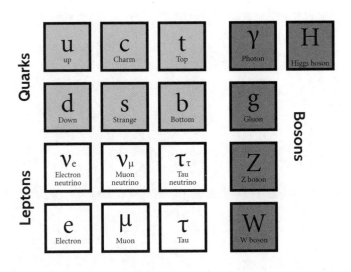

The elementary particles of the Standard Model including the quarks (mid-grey), the leptons (white), which constitute normal matter, and the force-carrying bosons (dark-grey) along with the newly discovered Higgs boson.

proton and an electron. Another feature shared by the lepton and quark 'matter' particles is that they all carry a quantum spin of exactly ½ and are called *fermions*. In addition to the fermions, there is a second family of particles called the *bosons*. These carry exactly 1 unit of quantum spin, but also serve a critical role in nature. They are the particles whose exchange between the fermions produces the fundamental forces of nature. The photon (γ) carries the electromagnetic force; the strong nuclear force is carried by a group of eight gluons (g); and the weak nuclear force is mediated by the W^+, W^- and Z^0 bosons, for a total of 12 elementary bosons. Finally, the Higgs boson (H), with a spin of 0, completes the Standard Model by interacting with all 24 particles to produce the property we call mass. The stronger the particle interacts with the Higgs, the more mass it appears to have. Photons and gluons do not interact with the Higgs and have no rest mass. However, the Z^0 particle interacts very strongly and has a mass of 91 GeV, almost 100 times the mass of a single proton.

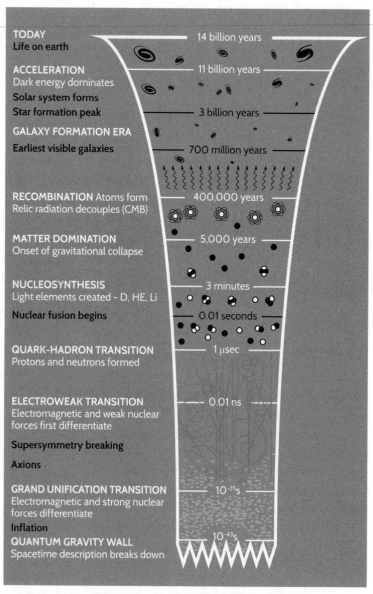

TODAY
Life on earth
— 14 billion years —

ACCELERATION
Dark energy dominates
— 11 billion years —

Solar system forms

Star formation peak
— 3 billion years —

GALAXY FORMATION ERA

Earliest visible galaxies
— 700 million years —

RECOMBINATION Atoms form
Relic radiation decouples (CMB)
— 400,000 years —

MATTER DOMINATION
Onset of gravitational collapse
— 5,000 years —

NUCLEOSYNTHESIS
Light elements created - D, HE, Li
— 3 minutes —

Nuclear fusion begins
— 0.01 seconds —

QUARK-HADRON TRANSITION
Protons and neutrons formed
— 1 μsec —

ELECTROWEAK TRANSITION
Electromagnetic and weak nuclear
forces first differentiate
— 0.01 ns —

Supersymmetry breaking

Axions

GRAND UNIFICATION TRANSITION
Electromagnetic and strong nuclear
forces differentiate
10^{-35}s

Inflation
QUANTUM GRAVITY WALL
Spacetime description breaks down
10^{-43}s

The timeline of the Big Bang and its major eras. Those eras before the formation of the primordial elements have been added based on our theoretical and experimental understanding of the Standard Model and its many internal interactions.

In addition to the Standard Model particles, there is a robust mathematical theory that describes in detail how forces are generated and how to calculate interactions among the particles via theories called Quantum Electrodynamics (QED) and Quantum Chromodynamics (QCD). It is the predictions from the Standard Model and the multitude of confirming measurements in high-energy physics that allow us to piece together a detailed model of the early evolution of the universe that extends with considerable confidence to a time far earlier than the first few seconds ABB. A synopsis of this evolution is presented here.

The basic idea that links these early eras together is that the CBR consists of photons that carry energy, and Einstein's famous equation, $E=mc^2$, relates energy to mass. If a photon carries enough energy, it can produce a matter–antimatter pair of particles, each with a mass of m if the energy of the photon is $Ep=2mc^2$. These particles can then combine and annihilate into pure energy as two photons, each carrying $Ep=mc^2$. The average energy of a photon is related to the current cosmic temperature defined by the two equations at the start of the chapter, so we can relate the time when the universe had a given average energy to the kinds of particle–antiparticle pairs it could produce. When the universe cools below the temperature where the CBR photons have enough energy to produce the particle pairs, the particle reactions stop, and the surviving particle–antiparticle pairs annihilate and are not replaced by new ones. Because there are a finite number of Standard Model particles of varying mass, there will be a small number of eras in cosmic history when they can be produced as particle–antiparticle pairs. The first such era we encounter is the Lepton Era. Note in the following discussions the mass of a particle is given by its equivalent energy via $E=mc^2$, so that $m = E/c^2$, but we set $c = 1$, and just report the mass of the particle in terms of its energy in electron-Volts.

THE LEPTON ERA

The lowest-mass lepton (disregarding neutrinos) is the electron with a mass of 0.51 MeV. Its antimatter particle, the positron, has an identical mass. So if the CBR photons have an energy of 2×0.51 MeV = 1.1 MeV (or 0.0011 GeV), they can produce electron–positron pairs. From our energy equation, this happened when the universe was just about one second old. The temperature then was about 10 billion K. At a slightly later time, these electron–positron pairs annihilated, but the photons carried insufficient energy to create new pairs, and so this mechanism stopped. The cosmos is left with only those electrons that it started with before one second ABB. The most massive leptons are the Tau leptons with masses of 1.77 GeV. Pair production required photons with twice this energy, which was available when the universe was $6×10^{-8}$ s old.

During the Lepton Era, we have protons, neutrons and the CBR photons interacting in a dense, hot plasma in which electron–positron, muon–antimuon pairs and tau–antitau pairs were being copiously produced and annihilated. The CBR photons were interacting with the slower-moving protons and neutrons to produce these pairs. But, as the universe expanded and cooled, each species of lepton pair vanished as its critical temperature was reached. In addition, the population of protons and neutrons was also changing dramatically. At the start of the Lepton Era, the ratio of neutrons to protons was one-to-one. But electrons colliding with protons caused them to change into neutrons and positrons (+ charged electrons); colliding with neutrons converted them to protons. The balance between neutrons and protons remained in equilibrium until positrons from the pair-production process started to decline as the end of the Lepton Era approached. The ratio of protons to neutrons then declined to one neutron for every six protons in an event called the Proton Freeze-out. This ratio declined a bit more to one-in-seven after the end of Nucleosynthesis Era, when free neutrons decayed into protons.

We would normally define the period between 1 s and $6×10^{-8}$ s ABB as the Lepton Era, but as it turns out there is a much more interesting and important set of events taking place at these earliest times.

THE QUARK ERA

The protons and neutrons are composed of quarks held together by gluons, so at some temperature (energy) the neutron–proton plasma dissolves into a quark–gluon 'soup'. From experiments at the Brookhaven Relativistic Heavy Ion Collider, this transition occurs at a particle energy of about 800 MeV. This occurred about 10^{-6} s ABB when the CBR temperature was 10 trillion K. After this time, it was cold enough that the quark–gluon plasma coalesced into the individual protons and neutrons. Before this time, the

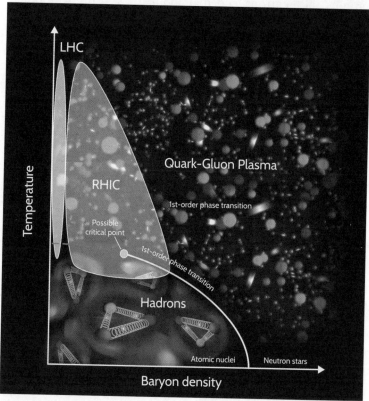

Phase diagram for the quark-gluon plasma. Much like water passes through solid, liquid and gas phases as temperature and pressure change, so too do the quarks and gluons that form the basis for nuclear particles such as protons and neutrons.

CBR photons interacted with the quarks and gluons to keep their energies above 800 MeV and the plasma acted like a gas. However, in terms of the density of matter at that time, the average density of the universe was everywhere equal to that of nuclear matter or about 10^{15} gm/cm^3. Despite these enormous densities, the plasma still acted in many ways like a gas of free particles. During the Quark Era prior to 10^{-6} s ABB, the CBR was able to pair-produce all of the different quarks and their anti-quarks.

So the era of the free quarks, and the building of the stable protons and neutrons, ended at about 10^{-6} s ABB. Astronomers consider that the Lepton Era started as a uniquely interesting epoch at 10^{-6} s ABB and not 10^{-8} s ABB. When did the Quark Era start? In actuality its beginning at a still earlier time is replaced by yet another significant change in the Standard Model.

THE ELECTROWEAK ERA

The prevailing idea in physics since the turn of the 20th century has been that the mathematical description of the forces of nature should be unified, meaning that these should be one mathematical theory that describes gravity, electromagnetism and the strong and weak nuclear forces. This idea is often expressed in the language of symmetry. In 1915, the German mathematician Emmy Noether proved that there was a relationship between symmetry and quantities that were conserved. For example, if the equation of a system is the same when you change the time variable from +t to -t, the energy of the system is conserved. This was later expanded to discover other symmetries in nature involving sub-atomic particles. An approach to unification developed by the English physicist Peter Higgs was to suggest that by adding a new field (particle) to a system, it could make the way that other particles interact dramatically change.

Because of their similarity in strength, the first pair of natural forces that were described in this way were the electromagnetic and weak forces.

This 'electroweak' unification was predicted in the 1960s in the theoretical work by Stephen Weinberg, George Glashow and Abdus Salam and is an important cornerstone for the Standard Model. The way that this works is that the particles that mediate the electromagnetic force, called photons, and the weak force, called the W and Z bosons, interact with the new Higgs boson, but they don't interact with the same strength. The photons do not interact at all, while the W and Z particles interact strongly. At first the Higgs bosons carry no mass and so the electromagnetic and weak force particles have zero mass and the interactions look 'unified'. But as the temperature of the system is lowered, the Higgs bosons gain mass, and so through their interactions the photons remain massless but the W and Z particles gain mass, and so the weak force starts to look very different from the electromagnetic force. In other words, the symmetry between the electromagnetic and weak forces is broken by their interaction with the Higgs boson.

The discovery of the Higgs boson at the CERN Large Hadron Collider in 2012 verified the core idea behind electroweak symmetry breaking, so that the energy at which this transition from three forces to the current four can be determined rather exactly.

The critical energy is about 250 GeV. What this means for the early history of the universe is that the CBR photons had an energy this high at a time 10^{-11} s ABB when the temperature was 3×10^{15} K. After this time, the fermions and the W and Z bosons had their currently measured masses. The weak and electromagnetic forces had distinct strengths with the weak force being about 10 million times weaker than the electromagnetic force as time moved forward. Meanwhile, the W and Z bosons, as well as the Higgs bosons, were being created and annihilated via pair production of the CBR photons because their masses are between 80 and 126 GeV, with the Higgs boson production ending as the universe cooled followed by the W and Z bosons. Before 10^{-11} sec ABB, we have only gravity, the strong interaction and the electroweak interaction as distinct forces with differing strengths.

What happens at even earlier times? Currently, the LHC can probe energies up to 13,000 GeV corresponding to a cosmic time of 5×10^{-15} seconds ABB. What has been found is that the Standard Model as it exists today still makes detailed and accurate predictions at these energies with no new particles or forces added to the theoretical mix. The search for new physics beyond the Standard Model takes the shape of many ideas including supersymmetry theory, string theory and grand unification theory. Each of these extensions makes their own predictions for how to extend the cosmic history story to earlier times. One of the basic elements that comes from all three approaches is the idea that eventually the strong force will merge with the electroweak force.

Based upon experimental data that shows how the electromagnetic and strong forces are changing strengths, and on a variety of theoretical models, the energy at which the strong and electroweak forces become identical in strength occurs at an energy of 10^{15} GeV. This energy is 100 billion times higher than the operating limit of the LHC. These energies were achieved at a time of 10^{-36} s ABB. Before this time, Grand Unification Theory (GUT) predicts that there were only two distinguishable forces in the universe: gravity and the GUT force. After this time, the GUT force dissolved into the strong and electroweak forces, and this split continued until the electroweak force finally dissolved into the separate electromagnetic and weak forces at 10^{-11} s ABB. But this GUT transition did more than merely alter the way forces behaved, it caused a major episode of expansion in the universe called Inflation that happened just after the GUT Era ended.

INFLATIONARY ERA

In order for GUT to work, a new family of Higgs bosons have to be proposed with enormous masses near 10^{15} GeV. But these Higgs bosons, just like the electroweak Higgs bosons with far lower masses, caused a change in the energy of the vacuum. The Higgs bosons interact with each other and are present everywhere in space. This means that 'empty space' actually has its own potential energy. What the Higgs fields do is to change this vacuum energy as the interaction energy changes. At low energy, the Higgs bosons gain mass, while at high energy they lose mass and become massless. This change is represented by an energy diagram.

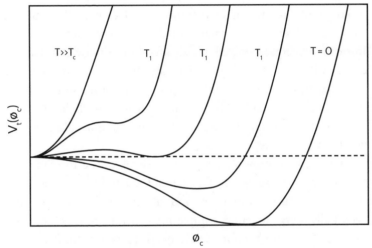

How the Higgs potential changes with temperature. At high temperature during the GUT Era (far left curve) the energy of the vacuum is simple, but as the universe expands and cools to zero-temperature (T=0) today, the vacuum energy curves change shape so that a new minimum appears with the lowest energy.

When the temperature is very high, the Higgs potential energy diagram has a parabolic shape with a vertex at the origin as shown in the first curve on the left for $T \gg Tc$. As the interaction energy decreases while the universe expands and cools, the potential energy curve changes until it takes the shape of the $T=0$ curve, which has a definite minimum. The horizontal axis represents the mass of the Higgs boson, ϕc. During the GUT Era the Higgs bosons had zero mass, but as the universe cooled by expansion, their potential energy curve changed so that eventually a local minimum was reached where they had masses of 10^{15} GeV. What was discovered by Alan Guth in 1980 was that this transition did not happen instantly, and the universe lagged behind the Higgs field change. The universe found itself in the vacuum state represented by the T>>Tc curve, while the Higgs field had changed to the low energy version with the minimum at φc. Physicists call this new vacuum state the True Vacuum because it has supplanted the older vacuum state. However, the universe was in a different vacuum state called the False Vacuum. How did this difference get resolved, physically? Guth discovered that the energy difference between the True and False Vacuum would act like a cosmological constant and cause the universe to expand in scale, exponentially. This would continue until the universe finished its transition to the True Vacuum and normal expansion would then resume.

The way to think of this period resembles the formation of bubbles in a carbonated drink. Each of these bubbles representing the True Vacuum would expand at the speed of light and eventually merge together, completing the transition as more and more of the False Vacuum was eroded. However, these bubbles would be embedded in the exponentially expanding False Vacuum space, so it would be a race to see if the entire universe switched over to the True Vacuum everywhere before the bubbles got so far apart that they could no longer merge due to the exponential expansion of the space between them. Guth's revised version called New Inflationary Cosmology repaired this problem by simply identifying one of these bubbles with the scope of our existing universe. The other bubbles represented other universes entirely.

Various calculations seem to indicate that this Inflationary Era lasted from about 10^{-36} s to 10^{-33} s ABB, allowing over 100 doublings in the scale of the cosmos. That means that the initial patch of spacetime prior to Inflation may have been 10^{-24} cm across, but afterwards this same patch, one among a multitude, would have grown to $2^{100} \times 10^{-24}$ cm $= 10^6$ cm. This does not sound like much, but by the time we arrive at 380,000 years ABB, this

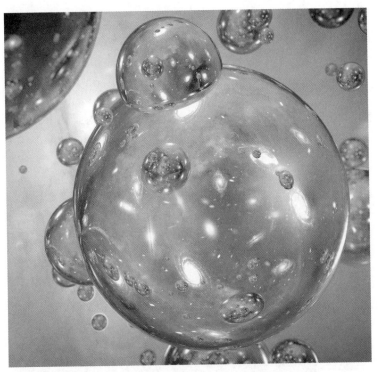

An artist's rendition of true vacuum bubbles forming in a false vacuum background.

inflated patch, once ordinary Hubble expansion resumed, had grown by an additional factor of 10^{27} times and would now be at least 10^{33} cm across. Our current visible universe is only 10^{28} cm across, so our visible universe is only 1/100,000 the size of the primordial, inflated patch. Guth discovered that this inflationary period eliminated the paradox that the CMBR is seen to be very uniform by the COBE, WMAP and Planck observations even though locations in the sky more than 1 degree apart could not have been in contact with each other until recently, and so the CMBR should be very irregular in temperature. It also proposes that there may be many other universes 'out there', each representing one of the other patches that existed before Inflation, but are now separating from us and each other by an exponentially expanding False Vacuum, which is still trying to reach the final minimum energy of the True Vacuum.

The exact details of how Inflation occurred and how long it lasted are still in dispute because they rely on the details of the theory for GUT physics for which no experimental tests are currently possible to decide between the many possibilities. Nevertheless, the GUT Era and the Inflationary Era that followed it are generally recognized as valid eras in the history of the early universe.

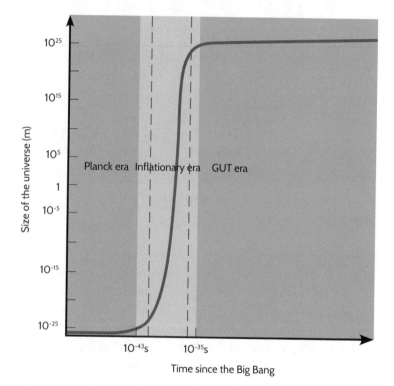

Diagram of the rapidly changing scale factor of the universe before, during and after the Inflationary Era caused by the change in the vacuum energy of space.

Key Points

- The temperature of the universe is determined by the temperature of the Cosmic Background Radiation, which increases as we look towards earlier cosmic epochs.

- Prior to the formation of the primordial elements, the cosmos passed through three major eras: The Lepton Era, the Quark Era and the Electroweak Era.

- The earliest times for which our current Standard Model for physics can be applied occurred at 1000 trillionth of a second after the Big Bang.

- Theoretical models of the unification of the natural forces suggests an additional GUT Era which occurred about 10^{-36} seconds after the Big Bang.

- The GUT Era ended during a period called the Inflationary Era when the scale of the universe increases dramatically.

Chapter 20

Cosmogenesis

In the previous chapter we discussed the Inflationary Era, which occurred as the Grand Unified Theory (GUT) Era came to an end. The Inflationary Era ended when the transition to the True Vacuum finished, but the way in which this happened has huge consequences for the Standard Model, and the way our universe looks today.

Theoretical modelling suggests that the transition to the True Vacuum occurred as the Higgs bosons gained mass, but GUT theories also suggest that other very massive particles called leptoquark bosons existed as well. These supermassive particles (10^{14} GeV) were spawned as the enormous vacuum energy of the Higgs field produced pairs of these massive particles, which would decay to the familiar Standard Model particles at a later time. The removal of vacuum energy by pair production of these supermassive particles may be the event that gradually caused inflation to come to a 'graceful' end, but when these supermassive particles annihilated, they caused a reheating of the universe to nearly the GUT energy once again... but not quite.

Today we find that we live in a matter-dominated universe with little or no antimatter to be found. The CMBR photons also outnumber the baryons (protons) by nearly one billion to one. This fact cannot be explained by any known process in the Standard Model, so cosmologically the origin of this asymmetry must have happened before the end of the Electroweak Era. One possibility being investigated is that it happened during the reheating of the universe after Inflation. At this time, there were supermassive bosons and leptoquarks present, and in some models for GUT there seem to be decay processes that favour more baryons than antibaryons. The detailed calculations are very model-dependent and as yet there is no experimental guidance as to which models for GUT are favoured.

The GUT Era ended with Inflation at about 10^{-36} seconds (s) ABB. However, the beginning of the GUT Era takes us to an even earlier time in cosmic history that may well be the final moment that can be discerned, where at last we come face-to-face with the actual origin of the universe itself.

THE PLANCK ERA

To describe this era we have to take a last step in physics by unifying the GUT force with gravity. For decades, the road to unifying gravity with the Standard Model has been fraught with difficulties. Chief among these is that the language of the gravitational force, represented by Einstein's theory of general relativity, is largely incompatible with the mathematics of quantum field theory upon which the Standard Model is based. One of the major difficulties is that the Standard Model and its extensions in string theory and supersymmetry theory are dependent on the four-dimensional spacetime of general relativity pre-existing. All the equations and formulations of quantum mechanics and the states of particles and fields use spacetime as a background framework and are therefore called background-dependent theories. General relativity, in addition to not being a quantum theory of gravity, is also manifestly relativistic. This means that space and time and spacetime itself are features derived from the relationships between bodies and do not pre-exist as some framework upon which gravity operates, which means that general relativity is background-independent.

A key feature of combining general relativity with quantum mechanics is that the gravitational field will be *quantized*. What this means is that the gravitational field of the universe, which we call spacetime, is composed of packets of geometry much like the electromagnetic field is composed of the packets of energy we call photons. To make general relativity a quantum theory of gravity we have to find a new way to describe gravity as the interactions among quanta of gravity. It is generally recognized from what is called 'quantum gravity theory' that this will happen at physical scales given by the Planck Units of mass, energy, time and space originally proposed as 'natural units' for physics in 1899 by Max Planck. These units can be formed by using the Newtonian constant of gravity (G), the speed of light (c), and Planck's constant (h), in the appropriate combinations to create the appropriate physical units as follows:

$$Lp = \sqrt{\frac{hG}{2\pi c^3}} \qquad mp = \sqrt{\frac{hG}{2\pi G}} \qquad tp = \sqrt{\frac{hG}{2\pi c^5}} \qquad Tp = \sqrt{\frac{hc^5}{2\pi Gk^2}}$$

When the appropriate values are used for these constants you get

Planck length $L_p = 1.6 \times 10^{-33}$ cm
Planck mass $m_p = 2.2 \times 10^{-5}$ g
Planck time $t_p = 5.4 \times 10^{-44}$ s
Planck temp. $T_p = 1.4 \times 10^{32}$ K
Planck energy $E_p = m_p c^2 = 1.3 \times 10^{19}$ GeV (or 2.0×10^{16} ergs)

Compare these units to the proposed GUT Era scales of 10^{15} GeV and 10^{-36} s just before the Inflationary Era begins and it is pretty clear that by the GUT Era at 10^{-36} seconds ABB we are very close to the scale at which the gravitational field itself displays quantum properties. The GUT Era is considered to exist between the Inflation Era at 10^{-36} s and about 10^{-43} s ABB, with the Planck Era occurring for times earlier than 10^{-43} s, if time itself is a meaningful concept.

During the GUT Era, there are effectively two forces that can be distinguished: gravity and the GUT (strong + electroweak) force. We do not know what kinds of particles were present, nor do we know just how much of the CBR was in existence. These details depend on the exact nature of the theory describing GUT unification, which is one of the areas being investigated in quantum gravity theory.

John Wheeler in the 1960s proposed that the gravitational field becomes a quantum field at the Planck scale in which its geometry is a superposition of possible geometries, and that the topology or shape of spacetime fluctuates wildly among many possible forms. This can be described as a foaming landscape where quantum black holes form and evaporate and wormhole-like connections and bridges turn spacetime into a dynamic Swiss cheese.

This conception for quantum gravity-scale physics is incomplete because it derives directly from general relativity and

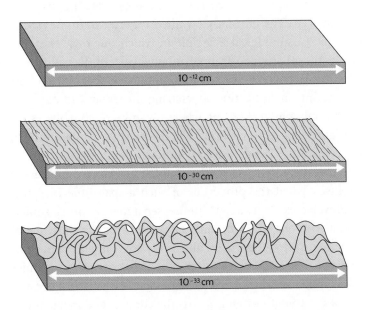

John Wheeler's quantum spacetime foam at the Planck scale. Because of quantum indeterminacy, the geometry of space fluctuated violently among many different possibilities, resulting in a topologically complex geometry for spacetime at the Planck Scale.

does not have a place for the Standard Model. There seems to be no way to go from this description to the idea of fermions and bosons as geometric features of this landscape.

Another approach is via *superstring theory* in which elementary particles are represented as one-dimensional 'strings' that vibrate in up to 11 dimensions, of which four are normal three-dimensional space and time. A tremendous effort has been expended in working out the details of string theory since it was proposed by Michael Green and John Schwartz in 1980, but this has generally led to no solid predictions that can be experimentally tested. It has also opened up the mathematical possibility that there are a multitude of self-consistent string theories that are possible but no way to discern why our particular 'solution' was selected for our universe. Instead there is a complex landscape of string theories for which some means of selecting ours has to be invoked. The currently favoured way to do this is via the Anthropic Cosmological Principle in which our own existence provides the missing constraint to uniquely specify the parameters of the string theory. A tremendous amount of theoretical effort has gone into investigating superstring theory and in applying it to the only physical setting where it can be reasonably tested: the origin of the universe itself. The theory requires spacetime to have as many as 11 dimensions within which our universe exists. Some investigators such as Lisa Randall at Harvard University have investigated the properties of such a spacetime in which our universe exists as a 4-D 'brane' separated by other similar 'Braneworlds' via the additional dimensions of the Bulk. All of the Standard Model particles and fields are trapped within our 4-D brane. The Randall-Sundrom model describes the dynamics of such systems and explains how gravity is a weak force because most of its strength extends across the additional dimensions of the Bulk. Cosmogenesis could also have occurred as these 4-D Braneworlds collide.

An important note, however, is that string theory already requires a background spacetime in which its string particles

Lisa Randall won first place in the 1980 Westinghouse Science Talent Search at the age of 18, and at Harvard University in 1987 earned her PhD in theoretical particle physics under Howard Georgi. She became the first tenured woman in the Princeton physics department and the first tenured female theoretical physicist at Harvard University. She is a prolific writer and popularizer of string theory, and her theoretical work involves baryogenesis, inflation, grand unification theory and general relativity.

operate, so gravity in the guise of the 4-D spacetime is merely a background. As we noted before, that makes string theory background-dependent and not technically consistent with the background-independent 'relativity' of general relativity.

Finally, the theory of *loop quantum gravity* (LQG) appears to solve the relativity problem by being completely background-independent from the start. The work by Lee Smolin and Carlo Rovelli has shown that, by borrowing some of the earlier ideas developed by Roger Penrose in the 1960s, you can create objects called spin networks. The vertices of these networks are quantized volumes of space, and the links between them are relationships that determine how much area is associated with each quantum of volume. In essence, space has dissolved into a collection of elementary points, and the geometric properties come from the relativistic relationships between these points. When spin networks are linked together to represent how one set of networks changes into another set, a new four-dimensional object called a 'spin foam' is created. At this level, four-dimensional spacetime has been fully quantized into discrete spin foams. The scale at which this happens is the Planck scale, and it leads to an interesting problem of epistemology; the study of knowledge and how we acquire it.

In quantum mechanics, if you want to study the state of a system you have to use photons whose sizes match the scale of the state being investigated. But photon sizes, called *wavelengths* (see page 11), depend on the energy of the photon; the smaller the wavelength of light the higher the energy of the photon required. If quantum gravity follows this same basic quantum relationship between size and resolution we encounter a severe problem. To probe the quantum gravity scale at 10^{-33} cm we need to use photons with energies equal to 10^{19} GeV. But these photons carry enough mass to become quantum black holes, which will evaporate after 10^{-43} seconds. This means that the Planck scale is a hard limit to the smallest scales we can ever probe to verify the accuracy of a theory of spacetime and gravity. If you wanted to 'see' what events look like at these scales, the light messenger would immediately turn into a quantum black hole and bury the information you seek.

Another feature of quantum gravity theory is that it does not provide an explanation for one of the deepest mysteries in physics: Why does time exist? As quantum gravity theory probes the deep

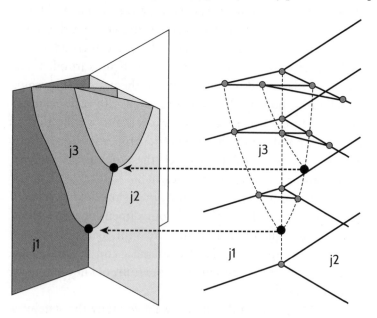

Organization of spin networks along a vertical 'time' axis to create spin foams.

structure of spacetime, it does not provide a clear explanation for why our four-dimensional spacetime isn't just a pure four-dimensional space in which the concept of ordered change does not exist. For example, your family photo album is a collection of two-dimensional photographs ordered in a three-dimensional format through the pages of the album, but this object is static. Although the photographs imply slices through a time-ordered sequence, the album remains a fixed space-like object. Each vertex in your family tree is a three-dimensional person. The lines you draw between these vertices express the information that one of these vertices is closer to one than another, but this 'closeness' is not closeness in space, but related to closeness in time.

Special and general relativity are based on the idea of four-dimensional spacetime, but this spacetime 'object' is eternal. Within it you can follow the entire history of a particle from birth

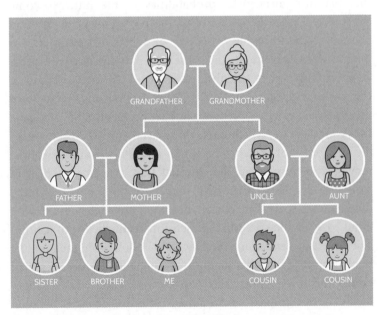

The relationships in a family tree represented by line segments are not relationships in space but encode time-like information while not themselves being 'time'.

to death as a complete worldline and see it from the 'all-at-once' perspective. This is called the Block Universe, and essentially eliminates time as an important concept. But nevertheless, we experience time, and moreover the present moment, as being very real. This leads to the conundrum that time is literally annihilated in the Block Universe perspective of Einstein's relativity, but is a vital ingredient to how we experience the world. This has been expressed by physicists as the problem of Now in the universe.

An intriguing explanation for time has been proposed by George Ellis. Experiments at the quantum level suggest that the Block Universe perspective of relativity is not correct. Although the past can be reconstructed from essentially classical physics and records of stored information (such as photographs), the future is closely determined by probabilities and principles found in quantum mechanics. According to Ellis, the 'present' is when the quantum mechanical probabilities of the future become 'crystallized' into the certainty of the past. This crystallization process seems to involve a variety of subtle processes such as quantum entanglement and observer participation operating at the foundation of the observable world. As for the origin of the universe itself, according to Stephen Hawking, a quantum mechanical tunnelling process may have occurred at the Big Bang. In its initial state, which could have been similar to the space-like attributes of the spin networks in LQG, cosmic spacetime may have been in a four-dimensional, pure space state. The spin foam we discussed previously may have been a purely four-dimensional space-like object. But then through a tunnelling event, one of the space-like dimensions tunnelled into a time-like dimension and, quite literally, time began. From then on one might suppose that the quantum entanglement process created events and sub-systems called 'clocks' from which state changes would be interpreted as on-going, time-like changes between states. Taking Hawking's idea one step further, the tunnelling event may have been irregular so that some regions of the pre-existing four-dimensional space may have remained unaffected while other 'bubbles' of the true spacetime may have formed with a time-direction.

So the Big Bang event during, or shortly after, the end of the Planck Era was the origin of three-dimensional space and of time itself, by some process that is currently not understood. We can surmise that the intense quantum fluctuations of spacetime (gravity) gave rise to the physics of the GUT Era by literally creating matter and energy out of 'empty' spacetime, but the details are currently not known.

Key Points

- Understanding the physics of the origin of the universe requires a deep understanding of gravity as a quantum phenomenon, which is described by Quantum Gravity Theory.

- The scale at which quantum effects in gravity and spacetime take place is characterized by the Planck Units of mass, time, energy and size.

- Two quantum gravity theories, string theory and loop quantum gravity, are incompatible because string theory depends on a pre-existing four-dimensional spacetime while loop quantum gravity does not.

- The origin of the dimension of time, and the physical definition of the moment called Now, remain deeply mysterious issues at the forefront of physics and cosmology.

- The Big Bang was the origin of space, time and matter represented by events taking place near 'Time-Zero' or at 10^{-43} seconds during the Planck Era.

Glossary

Arcsecond – A basic angular measure in astronomy equal to 1/3600 of a degree of arc.

Astronomical Unit – The average distance between Earth and Sun equal to 149 million km (92.6 million miles).

Big Bang – The name used to describe the cosmological model based upon Einstein's theory of general relativity, more properly called the Friedmann-Lemaitre-Robertson-Walker cosmological model

Black hole – An object predicted by general relativity whose spacetime curvature is large enough to prevent light from escaping at a distance from its centre defined by its event horizon.

Black-body spectrum – The unique energy distribution of electromagnetic radiation that occurs when an object is opaque to its own emission so that the electromagnetic energy can thermalize with the matter in the object at a unique temperature.

Boson – A class of fundamental elementary particles that possess an integer unit of quantum spin such as photons, gluons and W and Z particles.

Cannibalism – The physical process by which a system gains mass at the expense of consuming neighbouring gas or other collections of matter such as stars or galaxies.

Cosmic background radiation – The population of photons generated by the events during the Big Bang, which form a gas of photons that permeate all locations within the cosmos.

Cosmological constant – A mathematical quantity added to Einstein's equation for gravity, which serves to prevent the collapse of matter at cosmological scales. Also called Dark Energy.

Dark energy – A condition of space similar to Einstein's cosmological constant, which causes the rapid expansion of space.

Dark matter – A 'substance' commonly detected in the halos of galaxies or in clusters of galaxies, which does not interact with or generate light but only acts through its gravitational force with other matter.

Degeneracy – A quantum condition involving fermions in which the particles of a plasma occupy all of the available quantum states for the system. An important force for the stability of white dwarfs and neutron stars.

Differential rotation – The manner in which a gaseous sphere attempts to rotate as a solid body, but lacks cohesion so that its equator travels faster than its polar material.

Electromagnetism – The force that acts between charged particles, which has both a magnetic and electrostatic character that changes with the relative speeds of the observers according to special relativity.

Exoplanet – A planet-sized object orbiting another star.

Extremophile – A species of bacterium which can survive under normally lethal conditions of temperature, salinity, or pressure.

Fermion – A class of fundamental elementary particles that possess ½ units of quantum spin such as electrons, neutrinos and quarks.

Field – Any physical quantity that has a distribution in space and can be characterized by unique values (scalar, vector or tensor) at every mathematical point in space.

Frost line – The distance from a star where exposed surfaces are cool enough that liquid water solidifies to snow or ice.

Fusion – The process by which two separate systems, usually nuclei, combine together to form heavier systems, such as three helium nuclei fusing together to form a carbon nucleus.

Galactic halo – The region of space surrounding a galaxy in which are generally found the oldest stars in the system.

Galaxy – A system of stars and interstellar gas that can contain upwards of hundreds of millions of stars, and considered the most elementary constituents of large-scale cosmic structure.

Habitable zone – The region surrounding a star in which temperature and surface conditions allow for water to be found in a liquid state suitable for living systems.

Hyperstar – A star with more than about 50 times the mass of our Sun.

Inflation – A physical process involving the rapid increase in the separations between material objects due to a change in the energy of empty space, called the quantum vacuum.

Interferometer – A telescope design in which pairs of telescopes combine their signals to form a new telescope with an equivalent diameter equal to the separation between the telescopes.

Lepton – An elementary particle of the fermion class which only interacts through the electromagnetic or weak forces such as electrons, muons, tauons and their associated neutrinos.

Light year – The distance travelled by light in one year equal to 9.5 trillion kilometres (5.9 million miles).

Luminosity – The amount of energy, usually in the form of light, emitted by a star each second, usually represented in units of watts or ergs/sec. One solar luminosity (Lsun=1.0) equals 3.8×10^{26} watts.

Magnetism – A force generated by currents of charged particles which has a handedness or 'polarity' commonly referred to as north or south.

Main Sequence – On a Hertzsprung-Russell Diagram, the diagonal band occupied by most stars in the sky, corresponding to the stable burning of hydrogen into helium.

Parallax – The apparent shift in the position of an object as seen from two different vantage points, usually measured in degrees of angle.

Parsec – The distance at which the parallax shift of an object equals 1 arcsecond or 1/3600 of a degree and equal to 206,265 Astronomical Units or 3.26 light years.

Photon – A quantum of electromagnetic energy characterized by its integer-spin (boson) and its wavelength.

Planck Era – A period of time in the history of the universe before about 10^{-43} seconds after the Big Bang when/where space and time can no longer be described by conventional non-quantum terms.

Planet – A large object that has swept out nearly all of the material in its surroundings and has no other nearby neighbours. Pluto is not a planet because it is still embedded in a significant debris field called the Kuiper Belt.

Planetesimal – A class of massive objects that are still accreting material from their surroundings during the planet-forming era in a solar system, typically about 500–1000 km (310–621 miles) in diameter.

Plasma – A collection of particles consisting of electrons, protons and the ionized versions of various atoms. Highly reactive to magnetic fields and exists at temperatures above 10,000 kelvins.

Primordial elements – The small collection of elements which could have formed soon after the Big Bang, consisting of hydrogen, deuterium, helium, tritium, lithium and beryllium.

Protostar – A large object forming at the centre of a disk of gas and dust into which matter is still in-falling and will eventually collapse to form a star.

Pulsar – A rapidly rotating neutron that emits bursts of radio energy in beams which can sweep across the direction of Earth and cause periodic radio signals.

Quark – An elementary particle of the fermion class which exists within larger particles called protons and neutrons, and which are held together by the strong force mediated by bosons called gluons.

Quasar – A distant galaxy in which a supermassive black hole is rapidly consuming matter and generating a luminosity equal to hundreds of Milky Way galaxies.

Radiation – The outflow of particles or energy from a source in space, which decreases in intensity according to the inverse-square law.

Spacetime – A mathematical concept in which the three dimensions of space and the one dimension of time are combined into a four-dimensional geometry within which all events in the cosmos occur along individual worldlines.

Spin network – In quantum gravity theory, a collection of points connected by relationships such that the point occupies a Planck volume in space, and the point-to-point relationships are represented as connecting line segments that carry a quantum of surface area.

Supercluster – A collection of hundreds of clusters of individual galaxies that travel through the universe as a single system.

Superstring – A one-dimensional loop of spacetime whose vibrations in 10 dimensions provide the properties of the individual particles and their interactions.

Tachocline – The region in the solar interior between the radiative and convective zones where plasma currents can form that generate the solar magnetic field.

Telerobotics – The technology that allows robotic systems such as rovers to be operated millions of miles away by humans.

The Bulk – The name given to the 11-dimensional spacetime in which our four-dimensional spacetime is embedded in a structure called a brane.

T-Tauri –A phase in the formation of a star characterized by the last stages in the accretion of matter onto the surface of a star including magnetic fields, which cause enormous flares and plasma ejection events.

Unification – The approach to elementary particle physics that says that there is a single comprehensive mathematical model that accounts for the properties of particles and the forces through which they interact.

Vacuum energy – Quantum mechanics requires that the vacuum be filled with a variety of 'virtual particles', and these particles and fields contribute to the vacuum having a definite non-zero energy.

Worldline – The three-dimensional locations of a particle connected in time form a four-dimensional line called the worldline, which starts at the birth of the particle and ends when the particle vanishes in the future.

Index

Picture Credits

t = top, b = bottom

Alamy: 176t, 188, 217

Brookhaven National Laboratory: 211

Daniel Pomarede: 184 (Yehuda Hoffman/ Hebrew University of Jerusalem)

David Woodroffe: 64, 223

ESA: 154 (Stefan Meingast/GAIA/DPAC), 170 (NASA and Hubble Space Telescope)

ESO: 59, 77, 108, 120 (Igor Chekalin), 135 (M. Kornmesser/ESA/Hubble), 161 (M. Kornmesser)

Getty Images: 19 (SSPL), 82 (Universal History Archive/UIG), 178 (New York Times Co.), 190 (Hulton Archive)

Hubble Space Telescope: 147 (NASA and ESA), 153 (David L. Nidever, et al., NRAO/AUI/NSF and Mellinger, Leiden/ Argentine/Bonn Survey, Parkes Observatory, Westerbork Observatory, and Arecibo Observatory)

Library of Congress: 21

NASA: 16 (JPL-Caltech), 17 (X-ray: NASA/CXC/SAO; Optical: NASA/STScI; Infrared: NASA-JPL-Caltech), 42 (AEI/ ZIB/M. Koppitz and L. Rezzolla), 54b (GSFC), 55 (JPL-Caltech), 62 (ESA/HST), 65 (SDO), 66 (GSFC), 78 (JPL), 80 (JPL), 86, 88 (John Hopkins University Applied Physics Laboratory/Southwest Research Institute), 91 (JPL-Caltech), 99 (GSFC), 118 (JPL-Caltech), 143 (ESO), 144 (ESA, AURA/Caltech, Palomar Observatory), 147, 150 (JPL-Caltech/ESO/R. Hurt), 155 (ESA, Z. Levay and R. van der Marel (STScI) and A. Mellinger), 156 (ESA and the Hubble Heritage Team (STScI/AURA)), 157 (X-ray: NASA/CXC/Univ of Crete/K. Anastasopou-lou et al, NASA/NuSTAR/GSFC/A. Ptak et al; Optical: NASA/STScI), 158 (ESA/ CXC), 159 (X-ray image by NASA/CXC/M. Markevitch et al.; optical image by NASA/ STScI, Magellan/U.Arizona/D.Clowe et al.; lensing map image by NASA/STScI, ESO

WFI, Magellan/U.Arizona/D.Clowe et al.), 162t (ESA, P. Oesch and I. Momcheva (Yale University) and the 3D-HST and HUDF09/ XDF Teams), 162b (CXC/M. Weiss), 165 (X-ray: NASAc/CXC/SAO, Optical: NASA/ STScI, Radio: NSF/NRAO/VLA), 168 (X-ray (NASA/CXC/Virginia/A.Reines et al); Radio (NRAO/AUI/NSF); Optical (NASA/STScI)), 169 (Andrew S. Wilson (University of Maryland; Patrick L. Shop-bell (Caltech), Chris Simpson (Subaru Tele-scope); Thaisa Storchi-Bergmann and F. K. B. Barbosa (UFRGS, Brazil); and Martin J. Ward (University of Leicester, U.K.)), 176b (X-Ray (NASA/CXC/CfA/E.O'Sullivan); Optical (Canada-France-Hawaii-Telescope/ Coelum)), 177 (ESA and the Hubble Heritage Team (STScI/AURA)), 196 (JPL-Caltech/GSFC/SDSS), 198b (ESA and A. Field (STScI) 200 (WMAP Science Team)

NOAO: 22 (AURA/NSF)

Science Photo Library: 31 (Royal Astro-nomical Society), 33b (Colin Cuthbert), 41 (Volker Springel/Max Planck Institute for Astrophysics), 58 (Russell Kightley), 68 (Royal Astronomical Society), 117 (Mark Garlick), 130 (Argonne National Labora-tory), 136 (NASA/Skyworks Digital), 179 (Emilio Segre Visual Archives/American Institute of Physics)

Shutterstock: 227

Sloan Digital Sky Survey: 183, 201t (Joel Primack, Anatoly Klypin/Bolshi Simula-tion, NASA Pleiades supercomputer)

Swedish Solar Telescope: 54t (Institute for Solar Physics, Sweden/Royal Academy of Sciences)

TNG Simulations: 201b

University of Cambridge: 100 (Amanda Smith/Institute of Astronomy)

Wellcome Collection: 27, 36, 37, 38,

Wikimedia Commons: 15, 20t, 23, 30, 33t, 48, 79, 131, 175, 186, 197